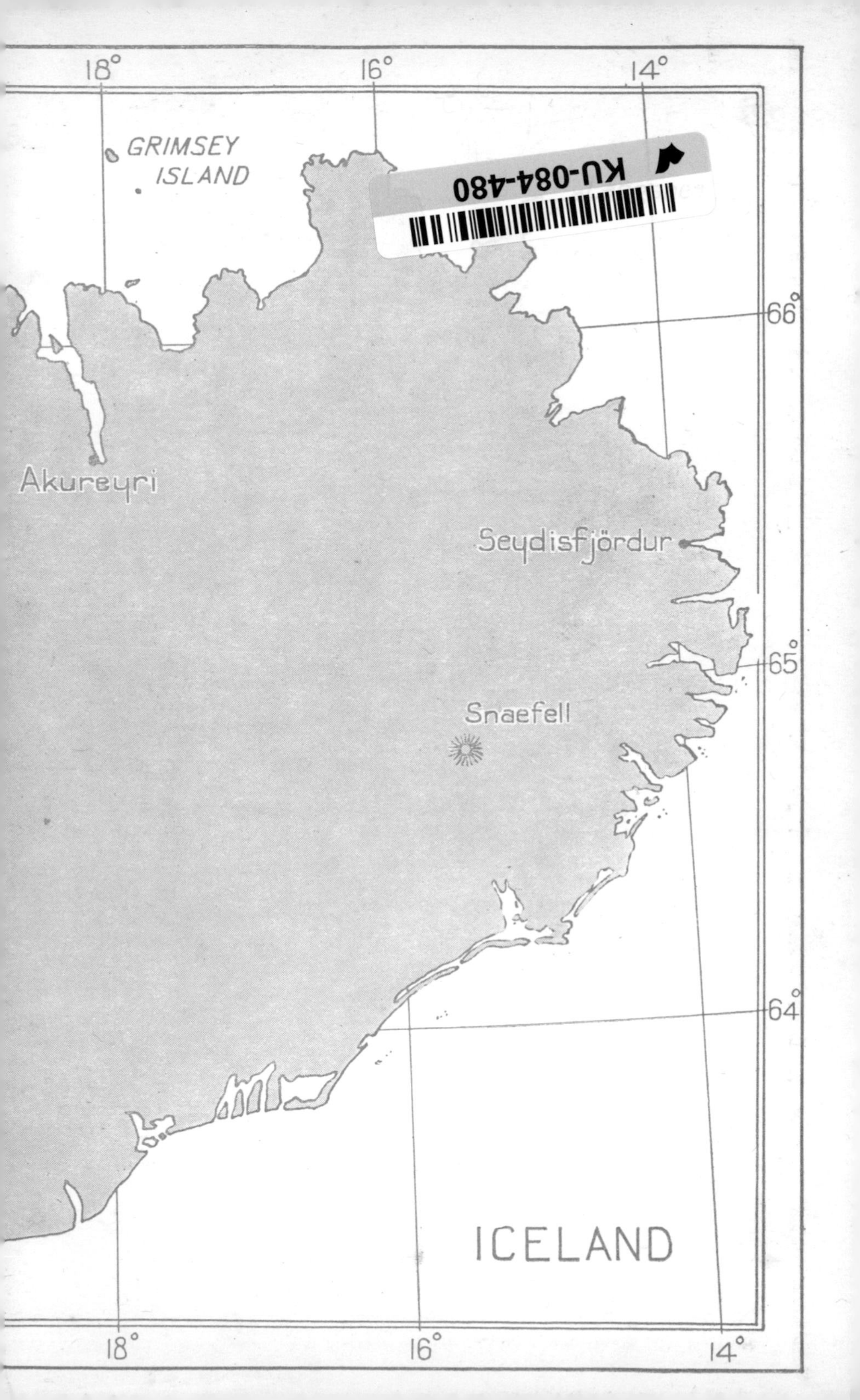
18°
16°
14°
GRIMSEY
ISLAND
66°
Akureyri
Seydisfjördur
65°
Snaefell
64°
ICELAND
18°
16°
14°

NORTH CAPE

N. & M. Cunninghame.

Aug. 1940.

Trawlerman.

NORTH CAPE

BY

F. D. OMMANNEY

Author of " South Latitude "

WITH TWENTY HALFTONE PLATES

LONGMANS, GREEN AND CO.

LONDON : NEW YORK : TORONTO

LONGMANS, GREEN AND CO. LTD.
39 PATERNOSTER ROW, LONDON, E.C.4
17 CHITTARANJAN AVENUE, CALCUTTA
NICOL ROAD, BOMBAY
36A MOUNT ROAD, MADRAS

LONGMANS, GREEN AND CO.
114 FIFTH AVENUE, NEW YORK
221 EAST 20TH STREET, CHICAGO
88 TREMONT STREET, BOSTON

LONGMANS, GREEN AND CO.
215 VICTORIA STREET, TORONTO

First Published 1939

Printed in Great Britain by the Kemp Hall Press Ltd.
in the City of Oxford

“ Wha’ll buy my caller herrin’ ?
They’re no brought here without brave darin’,
Buy my caller herrin’,
Ye little ken their worth.”

“ Wha’ll buy my caller herrin’ ?
O ye may ca’ them vulgar farin’ !
Wives and mithers, maist despairin’,
Ca’ them lives o’ men.”

LIST OF ILLUSTRATIONS

CHAPTER I

THERE is something different about a seaport town. There is a special atmosphere in the streets which is not due simply to the glimpses you get of masts and coloured funnels between buildings, or of giant cranes leaning beyond the roof tops. Nor to that vagueness in the sky over the houses in one direction as though, if you went that way, you would come to the very edge of the world. It is something about the people, the way they walk and the way they look at you, which is different from the manner of other people in other towns.

When you get out of the train at Grimsby you find yourself in what seems to be the usual north midland English industrial town. A feeling of chill desolation settles upon you at once, for the architecture of those forbidding streets seems to shut out all hope. You cannot imagine, in the first place, how people can have set to work seriously to build such a town, nor, in the second place, how, having built it, they managed to induce their fellow creatures to live in it. What was going on in the minds of the architects who designed those edifices, at once ponderous and mean, that serve for public buildings? And how could anyone have set brick upon brick to make those interminable rows of blank-faced little houses and then, having made them, have invited people to live and grow up, love and die in them, calling them by the sacred name of home? As you go through those streets towards the sea the houses become meaner and still more drab. Here are those forlorn places of entertainment which by night flower into a splendour of illumination. They have grand names borrowed from Italy via America—the Rialto, the Plaza, the Rex. No one knows what those names mean but by night, under the lights, they lend a kind of glamour to the dingy brickwork. And here are all those pubs around which sad little knots of people wait all day hopelessly for the doors to open. Yet, mysteriously, there is a change coming over these streets as you pass through them. For over there, beyond the squalid alleys, the warehouses, the railway sidings and the cranes, is something infinite and old, that moulds the lives and thoughts, the hopes and fears, of all the sturdy, soft-voiced people that pass to and fro among them. There is the sea—their life and death, their salvation and their doom. There is no escape from it. It possesses them so completely that most of them would not forsake it if they could.

This town, indeed, is just a kind of annexe to the sea, belonging to it as much as the foreshore or the cliff-face with its teeming population of birds. Men come ashore here like birds to build their homes and to stay only a little while between long days or weeks at sea, during which their thoughts are always turning towards the cliff-face and its real or imagined joys.

" Me ? I live in Grimsby, I do. Wouldn't mind bein' there now an' all."

But what that means really is that in a street in Grimsby is a little house kept by a hard-working woman on the money her man brings in after many days at sea. He has the right, on that account, to put his feet up there. Or to come back late, singing, and flop upon the bed, to sleep with the woman who keeps the house, or to stand with a proprietary air before the door of a Sunday morning in a blue serge suit and a check cloth cap. There are children in the house, maybe, begotten in these brief hours of return and born in absence between two home-comings. They become older and bigger and less familiar every trip. But what man can say that he lives in Grimsby of all the cloth-capped crowd that throngs its grey streets? They amuse themselves there, get drunk and fight and whore and go back to sea again where they belong. Or they put their feet up in homes they do not really know and enjoy unaccustomed luxuries for a little while. But they live beyond the north wall and the lock gates, down the muddy Humber River, beyond the lightship with its triple flash.

Only when he gets too old for the job can the fisherman be said to live in Grimsby. Then he is "on the corner," one of a sad little crowd hanging around with dull eyes near the labour exchange or round the pub doors, flotsam thrown ashore by the sea. Even then he does not really belong there. He belongs nowhere in particular.

Any evening down at the Fish Dock you may see the trawlers returning one by one in a long slow procession through the lock gates. They are coming in for tomorrow's market and early in the morning they will

" land," or unload, their fish, the harvest of days or weeks at sea. Their masthead lights shine faintly now as they move in, a long string of them one behind the other. The smoke from their funnels goes up on the evening air. The women gather in the streets about this time, their clothes bright against the brick-work, bright blue and russet brown, as they turn in towards the dock, laughing, to welcome back their men. Each trawler noses her way in silently to her berth, bringing with her something of the strange aloofness and mystery of the sea. Her trawling boards are stowed beside the gallows, her trawls snug along the rails. Her decks are clear and swept and her fish hatches battened down. The men on the whale-back, or fo'c'sle head, move in silence at the mooring ropes. One of them throws a heaving line to a man on the jetty. On the quay a man with a megaphone is bawling across the echoing spaces of the dock.

" Right up to the end, *Northern Pride*! . . . Farther along, *Northern Pride*! . . . There's the *City of York* comin' in astern of you. . . . Get a line round that bollard, *City of York*! Close astern of *Northern Pride* . . . Right! That'll do. . . Up beside *City of York* there, *Margaret* . . . Whoa! That'll do."

On the whale-back the men straighten themselves and laugh down at the women.

" Well, 'ere we are an' all."

" Thought you was lost. Where've you been all this time? "

" How you keepin', Kate?"

" Can't grumble, Jim. How's yourself? "

It is home-coming. Every man is soon ashore in

his blue serge suit and check cloth cap, the regular shoregoing rig for fishermen in Grimsby, his kit-bag over his shoulder, leaving the ship deserted. Only the water rushing from her condensers breaks the night silence of the dock. The little company, whose home she is, are scattered in that dim confused region of light and shadow beyond the gates where holes are so easily burnt in pockets.

At half-past three next morning the " lumpers " come down to land the fish, clattering over the paving stones in their heavy metal-shod boots. All the echoing spaces of the dock break into a rattle and clangour of activity. The crew should be there too to help to land the catch. But you do not feel much like turning out at three-thirty in the morning after the first night ashore. So you lie in bed and forfeit twelve and sixpence which is the penalty for not turning out. But it is worth it to lie in bed listening drowsily to other men, for once, clattering to work.

The catch is all landed, stacked in boxes and away before noon when the tugs take the ship round to the other dock to fill up her forward fish hold with ice. In the afternoon they move her round to the coaling derricks in the outer basin. Before dusk she is lying alongside the north wall or the south jetty with ice and coal in her ready to sail again early the following morning, thirty-six hours after her arrival full of fish.

Along the north wall are the North Sea trawlers, lying side by side and filling the sky with their masts. They are small ships of a hundred tons or so and most of them are fairly old. They have the look of veterans, growing old in service, for the North Sea trawling does not pay too well nowadays.

The banks where the cod and haddock and plaice and other bottom-living fish have been taken for so many years are becoming fished out and the fish are allowed no chance to reproduce themselves there. This state of affairs had been approaching before the war but while, for four years, their enemies were hunting each other on and under the surface of the North Sea the fish had a holiday and recovered themselves on the banks. So when mankind gave up the silly business for a bit and turned his attention to the fish once more there was a rich harvest waiting for him. But, by the exquisitely simple equipoise which Nature preserves, the increase in the number of fish automatically reduced their food supply so that all the fish, though more numerous than before, were smaller in size. But there is no sense in what men do and so the banks are becoming empty of fish again through the unorganized rapacity of those who live by fishing. However, perhaps the fish will soon be able to rest once more, this time for ever. But for the present the catches that these grimy, gallant little ships bring in scarcely pay their running expenses. So old are they becoming now that they nearly all need new boilers and yet the cost of such an operation would in each case be greater than the value of the ship. So gradually they are going to the breakers one by one, these gallant sturdy little warriors that have weathered North Sea gales and outstared the fogs of winter and gone wallowing, beating back and forth from equinox to equinox for so many years. As a result many good,

North Sea trawlers, Grimsby.

hardy men, with soft voices and kind eyes, are " on the corner " in their old age, out of a job in the evening of a hard life. They stand about in melancholy little crowds opposite the labour exchange in Riby Square. And all the young, able-bodied men have forsaken the North Sea trawling for the deep water trawling. They sail in the big ships of three or four hundred tons that work the banks round Iceland, Bear Island, the White Sea or the Faroes. There are not so many of these sailing out of Grimsby (many more sail from Hull) so that competition is pretty keen and a skipper or mate must be smart at his job to keep himself continuously in work in the deep water trade. Any one of the deck hands will tell you how easy it is to find yourself on the corner.

The deep water trawlers lie rather aloof at the south jetty on the other side of the basin, opposite the North Sea trawlers and the little Danish seine-netting boats, where fair-headed youths bend over their nets and salute you as you pass.

It was at this wooden jetty that the *Lincoln Star* lay when I went aboard early one fine autumn morning. A little white feather of steam danced from the valve at her funnel. I had to clamber over the deck of the *Queen Eleanor* to get to her.

I arrived in a high-backed Daimler taxi, open to the view on all sides, feeling like royalty as I drove through the crowds of dock hands going to work—except that no one took the slightest notice.

" Wouldn't mind leaving the car here and coming with you," said the taximan affably, flinging my kit-bag down on to the deck of the *Queen Eleanor*.

"Well, you'd still find it re when you got back," I said. "No one would p ch the bloody thing, I bet."

I felt better after that. fter all it was only a quarter-past six in the mornir and only a cup of tea, brought to me by a heavily b athing night porter in the hotel, stood between me a d night starvation. I had been told to be on board b seven and so, as is my habit, I had allowed myself enty of time. I am one of those people who resent e speed at which we have to live but the only visible ffect that my resentment has, as far as I can see, is lead me to spend a disproportionate amount of time icking my heels on railway stations, where I always rive much too early for my train, in dentists' and doc rs' waiting-rooms, where I am always much too early r my appointment, and in other people's houses where lways appear long before I am expected. And on thi ccasion I arrived much too early for my ship so that hen I clambered on to the deck of the *Lincoln Star* I und no one there but a young man washing down the eck with a hose.

It is useless ever to try to projec oneself in imagination into the future, or to try to icture how one will behave or conduct oneself on ccasions still in the womb of time. I have known th for years but it does not prevent me from constantly aking thought for the morrow. Accordingly I had p epared several excruciatingly funny jokes which I p posed to fire into the air like rockets on my arriva on board the *Lincoln Star* and which I conceived wo ld make me immediately *en rapport* with anyone wh might have the good fortune to be within earshot. They would demonstrate what a one I was. But alas! There was only the young man washing down with a hose, who looked at me with a pair of steady grey eyes without a trace of surprise in them.

"You'll want to put your gear up there, I suppose," he said, indicating the bridge.

My pleasantries, foetal, stirring within me, almost ready for birth, were stillborn.

"Anywhere out of the way," I said.

A small vertical companion ladder led up to the bridge from the main deck. A narrow railed deck surrounded the wheel-house, a sort of pleasaunce where you could lean on your elbows and gaze forward over the well-deck to the fo'c'sle or aft along the engine-room casing and the sweep of the after deck. The wheel-house doors opened off this railed gallery. Inside the port door of the wheel-house a steep companion led down to the skipper's cabin and on the right of that was another door leading into the wireless room, a tiny box of a place, half of which was occupied by the baffling confusion of a radio transmitting and receiving set and the other half by a bunk. The young man dumped my kit-bag inside and locked the door.

"I suppose it can stay there till I know where my berth will be," I said.

"Ain't you the new wireless operator?"

"Well, no—as a matter of fact. Do I look like one?"

"You must be the chap that's goin' the trip, then?"

"That's right."

"Well, I hope you'll enjoy it. You'll find it a bit monotonous I expect."

"I dare say. You coming?"

"Me? Oh, no. I ain't comin'. You see—it's my eyes." He took the cigarette I offered. When he did so I saw for the first time the hands of a fisherman. I was to see many such hands in the next few weeks, the hands of labour itself, short, square, gnarled, the fingers always a little bent, the nails broken. The innumerable small wounds and scars of toil were upon them. I was to know the granite-like downright grip of them, hard as iron and rough as emery, when I grasped them in farewell. "You see—it's my eyes," he said, giving me a light and shading it with his two hands as he did so in the way all fishermen do. "I tried for my mate's ticket but couldn't get it on account of my eyes. Jim, the mate of this ship—you'll meet him directly—and me was at school together and we went up for our tickets at the same time. He got his so he's all right, but I got turned down along of my eyes. So now I work in the dock and mind the ship when she's in. Aye. I used to be in the North Sea ships but there's no money in them for a young chap. Well, they'll be down soon, I expect—the other chaps. I'll wait here till they come aboard and then I'll have to be getting along. You'll be sailing around half-past eight, maybe. You've to go to Blyth for coal. There's no coal here on account of the Doncaster races. The miners has a holiday for the races so there's no coal. Well—I must be washin' down. The Skipper'll show you where your berth'll be. He'll be down soon. I must be gettin' on with the job."

"I'll just wait around here," I said. He went clumping away in his heavy boots and was soon swishing his hose around the well-deck with a kind of fierce concentration as though the success of the trip were dependent on that humble service. I waited on the little railed bridge-deck, smoking cigarettes and listening to the early morning rumbling of my stomach and wondering why this young chap, so instantly friendly and natural in manner, should have these quite gratuitous difficulties placed between him and the attainment of his unassuming goal. Not for the first time I felt that indignation with the world, so righteous and altogether praiseworthy, if ineffectual, which always burns bright like a hot coal on an empty stomach.

From where I alternately stood, leant or paced up and down, waiting for someone to arrive and for something to happen, I could take in almost at a glance the lay-out of the ship which in the coming three or four weeks was to be my home. All trawlers are much the same in general plan and differ from one another only in size. Some of the North Sea ships are more grimy and squalid than others, and some of the deep water ships make more concessions than others to the amenities of life. There was nothing to show that the *Lincoln Star* conceded much in this direction. She seemed forbidding enough. She would roll like a bitch, I thought. Everything about her, ropes, rails, and stanchions, was covered with a film of coal dust and grease so that I soon found that cleanliness was a form of godliness almost impossible to achieve. Yet some of the northern boats, built in Germany under a barter arrangement and transferred to the British flag, boasted extraordinary and unheard-of luxuries, such as bathrooms for their skippers—unprecedented extravagance! But in all of them, and in the *Lincoln Star* as in the others, there was the same general arrangement. There was the relatively very large forward well-deck where the sorting, gutting and washing of the fish would be carried out. In the middle of the well-deck four square hatches, now covered over and battened down, led to the fish-hold below in which the fish would be stored away in ice. For'ard on the port and starboard side, immediately abaft the break of the fo'c'sle, were the hoop-shaped steel trawling gallows while aft there were similar gallows on each side abreast of the engine-room casing. Amidships, immediately below the bridge, were two steam winches from which the trawling wires, stout steel hawsers, ran forward to bollards on either side of the foremast. One wire ran to the pulley block on the forward gallows while the other ran round a second bollard back along the scuppers to the pulley block on the after gallows. The trawls themselves lay snug along the rails on either hand.

Men were beginning to arrive now one by one, clambering over the deck of the *Queen Eleanor* with their kit-bags. Almost every one wore a blue serge suit and cloth cap. One or two wore a collar and tie but most wore chokers round their necks. They looked up at me, where I lounged above them, with a mild interest but, again, without surprise and carried their kit-bags for'ard. I felt extraordinarily out of place and, not for the first time since I had arrived in Grimsby, somehow foreign. I knew that I bore no resemblance to any of these people and that, to

Lincoln Star.

them, I must appear like another species altogether.

Presently the same processional Daimler that had brought me here and left me stranded an hour ago drew up again on the jetty. A tall thin young man got out, paid his fare and came over the deck of the *Queen Eleanor* with a suitcase and a bundle of books done up with string. He was dressed in a shabbily smart suit, double-breasted waistcoat and patent leather shoes with improbably long toes. His tie stuck out from above the waistcoat like the handle of a tea-pot. He had a thin, pale, intelligent face and a certain charm of expression, a mildness that was immediately likeable. At the same time the face was melancholy when in repose. When he smiled, which was almost always, his mouth reached from ear to ear, displaying large white regular teeth, and his dark eyes all but disappeared into his head among the wrinkles that ran out from them. He almost always wore some variant of this exceedingly amiable grin, so that the contrast between his face when thus adorned and the strange sorrow that seemed to settle on it in repose was all the more remarkable. It made interesting what was, I daresay, really a very ordinary pleasant north-country countenance. He was the wireless operator, a fact which, to me, made his amiability all the more astonishing, and the melancholy, perhaps, understandable.

He, like all the others, appeared not in the least astonished at my presence. I began to get used to this philosophical acceptance of my existence. Perhaps, after all, it was not so astonishing as you might think to find gentlemen of foreign appearance and sinister aspect lounging about the deck in the small hours (they seemed small to me anyway) with no adequate explanation of their presence. And when he opened the door of his tiny cabin and found all the floor space occupied by my suitcase and kit-bag, he seemed to find nothing extraordinary in such a state of affairs. I hastened to explain.

"He thought I was the wireless operator," I said. "That's why my gear is in your cabin. I'll take it out of your way when the skipper shows me my berth."

"'E thought you was wireless operator?" he said, in a broad Lancashire accent. He looked at me incredulous for a moment and then gave me the first sample of that enlivening grin. "Oh, bloody 'ell!" And he burst out laughing. I wondered what one has to look like to resemble a wireless operator and in what way I had so obviously and dismally failed to come up to the mark. Anyhow the mere idea of my having been taken for one was so ludicrously funny that I did not live down the joke for days.

"D'you know? 'E was taken for wireless operator," he would say. "Oh, bloody 'ell!" And would lead the applause, if any, to this monstrous drollery by throwing back his head and laughing up to the sky in a way he had.

Now, having glanced round his tiny cabin, he unpacked his bundle of books and arranged them in a row on a shelf over his bunk. It seemed to make the little cubby-hole immediately habitable for him, the performance of this little preliminary rite. He stood back a bit and looked at them. "There," he said proudly. "I like a good read, I do." They were all sea stories, I noticed, of the more straightforward kind, usually, I discovered later, with a strong love interest provided by the boy-saves-girl theme.

" The skipper'll be along soon," he said when he had done this. " He'll show you your berth."

The skipper was at that moment arriving. I had already met both him and his mate, who had come aboard some time ago, the previous day in the owner's office. That had been an occasion calling for a certain amount of assurance on my part—a quality I summon up from the depths only on very rare occasions. The office was in the Fish Dock Road, a dismal channel with warehouses and offices on one side and hoardings screening a railway line on the other. A crowd of men surrounded the entrance and completely filled the narrow passage. I pushed my way in among them. There was a door bearing the owner's name on a glass panel. I knocked.

" Well," said a voice impatiently from inside. I walked in. The owner behind his desk was addressing a sturdy young man who stood before him folding his cap in his hands.

" . . . I leave it to you, Jim," the owner was saying. " You must do your best, that's all. I leave it to you."

" I'll do my best, sir. Thank you. I'll certainly do what I can," he replied in a soft, slow voice, and departed with every appearance of relief. He was the mate of the *Lincoln Star* though I did not know that at the time.

" I'm afraid I've butted in on you," I said apologetically when the door had closed.

" I don't usually allow people to burst in on me like

that," said the man behind the desk. " But since you're here, what is it? "

It was not until afterwards that I learned what an offence it was that I had committed in walking into the presence thus unannounced. I acquired by this act of ignorance a reputation for bounce which I knew I did not deserve.

" I wrote to you," I explained. " You were good enough to say that I might take a trip in one of your trawlers."

" Of course, I remember now. Do you want to go to Iceland or the White Sea? If you want to go to Iceland you can sail to-morrow morning in the *Lincoln Star*—eight-thirty. If you want to go to the White Sea you'll have to wait till Friday."

" Then I think it'll have to be Iceland. I'm very much obliged to you I'm sure."

" You understand, of course, that you're not to interfere with the working of the ship in any way whatever. And if the skipper tells you to keep out of the road, you must keep out of the road. Is that clear? "

" Of course."

" And there's another thing. These fishermen are the finest chaps in the world, but they're rough. They won't come up to your level, you'll have to come down to theirs. You understand that, do you? "

" Yes," I said, a trifle astonished to find that I had a level that was any different from anyone else's.

" Well, you seem to be the type. I hope you'll enjoy it." He pressed a bell. " See if Skipper Ellis is in the office anywhere."

When Skipper Ellis came in he undid for me all my preconceived ideas about trawler skippers. He was a young dapper little man with red cheeks and sleek, shiny hair. He wore a rather natty suit and a gold-wristlet watch. I could imagine him selling motor-cars or having to do with insurance, but not for a moment and by no stretch of the imagination would I have connected him with fish.

"This gentleman's going to make the trip with you. He understands that he's not to get in your road and when you want him out of it you can tell him so."

"Oh yes? Well, that'll be all right."

I let myself out from the presence. It was like leaving the headmaster's study, a poignant though long dormant sensation.

In an office farther down the passage I signed on at a shilling a week. "F. D. Ommanney. Age 35. Deck-hand. Previous ship, *Discovery II.* The other men waiting to sign on laughed and said, "You'll earn it, lad. You're a fisherman now."

CHAPTER II

THE methods of fishing at sea, as in fresh [illegible]ter, vary a great deal according to the manner of lif[illegible]of the fish. But on the whole the food fishes of the o[illegible]an are less varied in their habits than are the fishes [illegible] the rivers and lakes. In any case the first consi[illegible]ration in fishing on a commercial scale is to catch a[illegible]nany fish as possible in the shortest possible time s[illegible] that nets are used much more often than lines. A[illegible] the line fishing, where it is still done, is of a special k[illegible]d. Off the coast of Newfoundland and, I believe, st[illegible] around parts of the Scottish coast, lines are used for [illegible]atching cod, ling and halibut. These lines may be of [illegible]ormous length, several miles perhaps, strung tog[illegible]her in fifty fathom sections. At intervals along t[illegible]m are short branches about two feet long called " [illegible]oods " which bear hooks baited with fish. Each [illegible]ishing schooner has a fleet of small rowing boats [illegible]alled " dories " which string out their lines at nigh[illegible] along the bottom and take them up again in the m[illegible]ning. In the Mediterranean tunny fish, too, are som[illegible]imes caught with lines. But most fishing at sea is don[illegible] with huge nets which ensnare thousands of fish at a [illegible]me. They have meshes of such a width that in genera[illegible] only fish of a marketable size are taken. They ma[illegible] be seine nets, trawls or drift nets.

Seine netting is usually done in shallow water [illegible]om an anchored buoy or from the beach itself. The s[illegible]ne is a net bag with two long wings at each side. [illegible]he upper margin of the net is buoyed so that it floats while the lower margin is weighted so that it sinks. When the seine is worked from the shore one end of it is fixed to the beach while the rest is carried out in a row-boat or motor-boat which makes a wide semi-circular sweep out from the shore and back again, paying out the net over the stern as it goes. Thus all the fish within the semi-circle are entrapped within the loop between the net and the shore and are presently pulled in, a fluttering silver harvest, on to the beach. Naturally only fish close inshore can be caught in this way. But the Danish seine-netters, such as those who work in and out of Grimsby, fish farther out from the shore using an anchored buoy to which they attach one end of their net. They let the boat drift down the tide, paying out the net as they go. When the net has all been paid out they tow the unattached wing back to the buoy and so make a great bag into which the fish are gathered. The fish they catch by this method are mostly plaice and they get them in fine fresh condition. But it is still only in shallow coastal waters that the seine net is used.

Away from the shallow coastal waters the fishing is done by trawling or drifting. A trawl is simply a net bag which is dragged along the bottom. It catches any kind of fish which lives on the sea floor. The cod, the saithe, the haddock, the hake, the turbot, plaice or sole—in fact any commercial North Sea fish except the herring and the mackerel—are taken with the trawl. The herring too may even be taken with small trawls of fine mesh, though trawling for herring is, I think, done more in the Irish Sea than on our eastern coast. The trawl is descended from the Seine net which the French fishermen, who invented it, began to improve by making it into the shape of a conical bag in the middle. They found that the bag worked better if its mouth were kept open by cross beams of wood. Thus the simplest form of trawl, the beam trawl, came into being—a rectangular metal frame to which a bag of netting is attached so that the frame forms the mouth of the bag. But the size of a trawl like this is obviously limited by the size of the rectangular frame which, if too big, is very cumbrous and unwieldy to handle on board ship. So the beam trawl has given place to the "otter" trawl which is used nowadays by all commercial trawlers. It is simply a net bag slung between two rectangular wooden boards. The bag has an enormously wide mouth formed by an upper rope, the "head rope," which carries a line of spherical floats to make it lighter, and a lower rope, the "foot rope," which runs over the sea floor. The foot rope is threaded with metal spherical bobbins or wooden rollers which prevent it from catching on rocks and which smash down marine growths that would tend to fill up the net with rubbish. The net tapers away to a narrow conical apex of finer mesh, the "cod end," in which the fish collect. The head rope and the foot rope, forming the mouth of the bag, are slung in the water between two rectangular "otter" boards, or "doors," wooden and shod with steel, which are towed behind the ship each on its own wire, one from the fore part of the ship, over the forward gallows, and the other from the after part of the ship, over the after

Trawling gallows and "otter" boards.

gallows. The boards are set obliquely on their wires so that they are forced apart by their passage through the water, pulling open the mouth of the bag.

It is this simple but ruthless instrument, ploughing its way over the sea floor between fifty and a hundred fathoms down, which is used to catch most of the fish we eat. Most of the ships that sail out of Grimsby, are trawlers. They go to the North Sea banks or, like the *Lincoln Star*, farther afield to the banks around the Faroes, the White Sea, Iceland or Bear Island.

But drifters also sail out of Grimsby. From Yarmouth and Lowestoft enormous fleets of drifters sail in the autumn during the herring season when the fisher girls follow the herring from Scotland down the coast. The herring and the mackerel, which are taken with the drift net, do not live exclusively on the bottom like the trawl fish. They swim about in shoals near the surface, especially at night when the drifters mostly take them. In the day-time, when they tend to sink again, they can be taken with small trawls towed at high speed. The drift net is simply a net curtain two or three miles long hanging in the sea from a line buoyed upon the surface. The meshes of the curtain are of such a size that the fish are held in them, jammed firmly behind the gills, and cannot move either forwards or backwards. You may see the drifters, their steadying sails set, waiting motionless day and night upon the cold bosom of the North Sea. At night their unwinking lights gaze at each other across dark miles, spanned by their invisible curtains hanging in the sea.

Sea fishing is a gigantic industry to-day. The steamship and the limited liability company have made it so. So have the mouths of millions who like their *sole bonne femme* with white wine sauce for dinner or their nice bit of haddock for tea. If fishing were a shore job, and if the people who worked at it lived in packed cities, I feel that money and machinery would have stamped the soul out of it long ago, but, since it is a trade which exists both because of and in spite of the sea, a certain sturdy human element remains, some trace of individuality, a touch of adventure still. For every trawler that goes to sea is in a sense a little separate endeavour, an individual effort. It is a miniature expedition, led by the skipper and his mate. To the equipment of each expedition the owners contribute one good stout ship and the fishing gear, the nets, the wires and everything required for catching fish. But in all other expenses the skipper and the mate pay a share—such, for instance, as the wages of the crew, the coal, the food, insurance, dock charges and so on. In all these the skipper pays a share of ten per cent. and the mate a share of seven and one-eighth per cent. Similarly they share in the profits of the sale of the fish in the same proportion. So that every trip the trawler makes is a little venture. A successful trip to Iceland or the White Sea making, say, a thousand pounds brings the skipper a hundred and the mate seventy odd pounds. A Grimsby deep water skipper may make perhaps eight hundred to a thousand pounds a year and a mate, perhaps, four or five hundred. They are known as the "principal sharers" since they pay a share in the expenses as well as receiving a share of the profits, but all the crew are to a certain extent sharers also. The bo'sn, or third hand, receives about fourpence in the pound of the total profits of the voyage, the Chief Engineer threepence and the deck-hands twopence. A deck-hand's wage is two pounds five shillings a week and in addition to that, at the end of a three weeks' trip to Iceland or the White Sea or Bear Island, he may pay off with ten or twelve pounds. And he may sign on again in thirty-six hours with all of it gone and nothing to show.

"Well, I dunno. Tarts an' beer—that's what it is." Only thus, perhaps, is life found tolerable.

Within his little kingdom the skipper is supreme. He is the leader of the venture, the head of the expedition. It is he who decides the movements of the ship, which banks she shall visit in the area she is working in, just where she shall fish and for how long. But, as in all ships, he depends a great deal on his mate and his bo'sn for the smooth and efficient working of the ship and for the happiness of the men in her. The mate is responsible for the stowage and condition of the fish, for it is his job to see that the fish are properly gutted and washed and correctly stowed away in the fish-room. It is the bo'sn's job, as in every ship, to see that the work on deck is smoothly done and that the men are contented. Only the skipper knows anything about navigation, as a rule, and the mate and the bo'sn anything about seamanship while the "deckies" are little more than labourers. They bring in the trawl. They wash and gut the fish. They stow it below in ice. But, apart from this humble necessary labour, carried out with gruelling persistence in every conceivable kind of weather, they know little and care less. They live for their thirty-six hours in port, the beer, the football, the tarts, which are the heaven-sent means of escape from the crushing monotony of life spent continuously at sea in a small and dirty ship, with long and irregular hours of work, in cramped and uncomfortable surroundings. All these things, which are the commonplaces of life in little ships, breed a roughness and a coarseness in men. Continual close contact with each other accentuates these as the rubbing of two limbs continually together may thicken and callous the skin. It breeds a familiarity with the physically grosser aspects of life. No desires remain unknown, no secrets are hid. The functions of sex and excretion take their normal place with the sun, moon and stars. But with it all there flowers a simplicity and kindness that is to be met with only among men who live strenuously, and sometimes dangerously, together.

Of all the kings that ever reigned in these little hundred-and-fifty-foot kingdoms one of the most sure of his position was Skipper Ellis, with his shiny hair and gold wristlet watch and natty suit, so unlike a fisherman in appearance and exuding a faint air of motor-cars and insurance policies. He came aboard the *Lincoln Star* that morning in a mood of cheerful though regal disdain. He was taking over a new ship for the first time and he did it like a general entering newly won territory and finding much to be desired in it. He ran his hand along the bridge rail and removed on his fingers a trail of black coal dust and grease.

" Filthy bloody mess! " he said with a grimace.

The skipper's cabin was below the bridge. You went down to it by a steep companion way from the wheel-house, stepping down as you did so into a well of stuffy stagnant air that had sat there in undisturbed contentment ever since the ship was built. The cabin itself was a mahogany-panelled little box of a place with a bunk and a settee, a table with a vase full of artificial flowers (clamped to the table so that no trick of the weather should deprive the owner of the cabin of this proud decoration), various drawers and cupboards. A lavatory, with a wash-basin and a pedestal, led off it.

" Don't think much of this," said the Skipper, looking round with distaste at his mahogany abode. " Why—in my last ship I had a bathroom, o—o—oh! the size of the whole of this cabin, glass mirrors with lights above and everything." But for myself I was interested to find such a thing as a lavatory with a wash-basin attached to the skipper's cabin in a trawler. It seemed a quite unexpected luxury to me. However, I soon gathered that the absence of a mirror with lights above it was unforgivable.

Skipper Ellis was one of the leading skippers in Grimsby. He had started in the job right at the beginning as a deck-hand and had worked his way up to bo'sn, mate and finally to skipper. He had made the three weeks' trip to Iceland or the White Sea ten or twelve times a year steadily every year since he was seventeen. He was now twenty-eight, so he had made the trip to Iceland, or alternatively to the White Sea, over a hundred times. He was one of the few skippers sailing out of Grimsby who were in the happy and cherished and envied position, that many skippers hope to attain but very few do, where the owners offered their ships to him, instead of sitting in their offices waiting for him to go, hat in hand, to them. This position he owed to a long record of very successful and profitable trips, bringing in often more than two thousand five hundred baskets. He owed it also to a singular astuteness and canniness. "I never take risks," he said. "It's very seldom necessary." And "I always believe in finding out what the other fellow knows." So he listened continually to the radio-telephone conversations of other skippers, shouting their catches and their movements to each other across the air, but he himself kept his own counsel and said nothing over the air at all. Also, from long experience, he knew the Iceland banks as well as he knew the little street in Cleethorpes where, on the fruits of his astuteness, his wife kept a comfortable little home and one child. In fact he was probably more at home on the banks than he was there, since so much more of his life had been spent on them than in that little abode of lace and photographs in silver frames. Never once, indeed, during the whole of the trip to the Iceland trawling grounds and back again did he use a sextant or take a bearing more accurate than a swift glance at a distant headland through the wheel-house window and another at the compass-card in the deck-head. The sextant lived permanently in a velvet-lined box in a drawer beneath his bunk.

"Never use it," he said. "Never need to, you know. Know the course too well to worry with things like that. But I can use it. Oh! I can use it all right. Nice thing, isn't it? Nicely made, I mean." And he fitted it back carefully and lovingly into its velvet nest, where it lies now no doubt and has not seen the light of day since that proud moment.

Skipper Ellis was a tough, sturdy little man. In spite of his appearing to do so he knew nothing of motor-cars or insurance but had a penchant for football and boxing. Photographs of boxers, crouching in offensive attitudes, their foreheads puckered into the customary grimaces of puzzled fury, quickly made their appearance on the mahogany bulkheads of the little cabin below the bridge. Names I had never heard before became almost household words. "Pity we're not going through the fjords to the White Sea," he said. "We always used to pair off and put the gloves on in the evening." And the prospects of the Grimsby football team were a subject for furious partisanship and hot discussion. I fell a bit behind during these debates since I found myself deficient in views about the way the new centre-forward was shaping and what was the matter with Grimsby's defence.

When the Skipper had inspected his cabin, and found it wanting, he came up into the wheel-house.

"Pokey little place," he said. I pictured him at once on the bridge of the *Queen Mary*. "Well, I suppose we'd better be going." He rang the engine telegraph. Men on the deck cast off the ropes from the *Queen Eleanor* and slowly, gently, with no fuss or disturbance at all, the *Lincoln Star* backed sweetly out into the middle of the basin.

There was an informality about this departure which made it more like driving a car out of a garage. Anyhow it did not seem in the least like the departure of a ship bound for Iceland. There is something tragic and heart-breaking about the sailing of ships. "*Partir est mourir un peu.*" I have seen Union Castle liners back gently away from the quay at Cape Town with the band playing "God Save the King." I have watched the Orients sail from Melbourne, the widening gap of water bridged by a thinning web of coloured streamers. Often I have stood alone witnessing those scenes, sharing the little deaths of strangers, their laughter and their tears. When the *Lincoln Star* went from Grimsby that lovely autumn morning there was no laughter and no tears. A few men on the quay beside the gates saw us go with no flicker of interest. What was a trawler to them, sailing for Iceland on a sunny morning?

The mate was at the wheel in his blue serge suit and cloth cap, judging by eye when to put the helm over, peering through the wheel-house window and working the small steering-engine wheel with one hand. We moved slowly across the basin and neatly edged out through the lock gates into the grey Humber. Here a fresh wind sent the first bursts of silver spray hissing over the bows. The *Lincoln Star* began to lift and fall a little.

"You don't have a tug, then, to take you out into the river?" I said, observing the pleasant informality of this departure.

"A tug? Oh, bloody 'ell!" said Sparks. He pronounced it "toog," and threw back his head to guffaw at the heavens. No further explanation was really needed to assure me that my question had been profoundly idiotic, but Jim answered slowly, gazing at me over the spokes of the wheel with sad grey eyes. A settled melancholy seemed to belong to him.

"No—well, where it is, like—see—comin' in an' out of here regular we get to know our way about pretty well, see? 'Course, if we was goin' in or out of some other port things might be different. Not that we'd need a tug, any road, ship this size, but likely as not we'd have a pilot. Now at Blyth, like, where we're goin' in for coal this evening, now there we'll have a pilot, see? We're not too sure of the way there, see, on account of not having been in there before. Rather I should say, I've been in there before, once, but I wouldn't undertake to go in without a pilot, like. . . ." And so on. Jim was thinking aloud. It was a habit of his. He thought in silence until you started a train of thought by means of a remark or a question. Then he began to think aloud, gazing at you all the time with melancholy grey eyes as though it were all your fault—which it was for having started him off. The difficulty was that the thoughts ran on for so long that everyone but he lost interest in them. Jim's thoughts were usually of his young wife and his two babies in the little house in Railway Road, Cleethorpes. He thought aloud about them a great deal, puffing at the cigarettes I offered him and leaning on the spokes of the steering-wheel. Before the end of the trip, when I bade this faithful and loving young husband and father farewell, I felt I knew almost all there was to know about that little home. I could see in my mind's eye every room in it. I had taken imaginary high teas in it with kippers and the babies in their high chairs, the fire flickering on the polished furniture. I has seen the babies bathed and put to bed. I had sat after those imaginary teas in front of the fire while Jim put his feet up on the tasselled mantel, smoking while his young wife sewed. I had enjoyed the delights of home life as Jim knew them in his short spells between trips, as he dreamt of them on the Iceland banks during the brief half-hours of sleep in the little cabin aft, or as he pictured them aloud, slowly puffing a fag and leaning on the spokes of the steering-wheel. The foam burst outwards fanwise from the bows and the grey horizon rose and fell. But Jim didn't see it.

One wet filthy day when Jim was at the wheel I said, " What would you give to put your feet up on that mantelpiece now, Jim, with the missus in her chair knitting? "

" Oh Christ! Dick," he answered. " What wouldn't I bloody well give? " And I knew that I had been unkind.

As we steamed out into the Humber and began to punch into the choppy sea, streaked with angry flecks of white, Jim said:

" It comes very 'ard when you've been home for a spell. Oh! very 'ard it comes."

CHAPTER III

" WHERE you fro-o-om? "

A voice called across the glimmering stretch of dark water as we drew in. High overhead in the early darkness towered huge and inhuman shapes, studded sparsely with lights that stood again in the water below. Coaling derricks, overhead railways, the masts and funnels of ships loomed blackly. There was a kind of menace about the silence of the place. Only a Tyneside voice broke it calling thinly in the darkness—" Where you fro-o-om? "

" Grimsby! "

We had beaten up the Yorkshire coast all day and at twilight stood before the confused jumble of lights which I knew was the port of Blyth. We blew for a pilot.

" Not much doing here these days," said the pilot. " Aye, things are pretty bad in Blyth." He was a stocky, thick set Tynesider with white hair and two rows of fine teeth. " Tell the truth, I don't think they'll get much better from the looks of things, what with all the pits closing around here and no ships comin' in. Keep they two lights in line, Skipper. Yes, you'll be coaling to-morrow morning likely. Get away about mid-day. A little to starboard, just a wee bit. Well, ye'll be able to get ashore and take a look at Blyth. Don't fancy you'll find much to it, though. Over there, under Number Three hoist. No, there's not much in Blyth. It's a pretty poor sort of place. The beer ain't bad, though."

" There's tarts, ain't there? " said the man at the wheel.

" Oh aye, there's them."

We slid alongside the jetty under the towering skeleton of a coal hoist that blotted out the stars, rearing its gaunt bulk up from black mountains of slag. Farther along lay other ships beneath other skeletons. Their lights shone dully in the water. We were in port again. Beyond the strip of glassy darkness that was the river, over there where the little dingy houses ran back in rows behind the elevated railway, was a region of shrill and cheap allurement. I could see lights there. For sailors they hinted at adventure, stale and unprofitable and old, yet ever new and ever exciting. Jim had strict orders from the owners that the men were not to be allowed ashore in this place of temptation and of snares. For, once in those frowsty bars and haunts of dreary joy up the back streets, it was likely as not they would never return in time to get the ship next morning. It had been a strict injunction on this very subject that I had interrupted when I walked into the office with such effrontery the morning before we sailed. " Use a marline spike on them if necessary, Jim," the owner had been saying, " but on no account let anyone get ashore. You must do your best—I leave it to you."

" Well, I'll do my best, sir," said Jim. " I'll certainly do what I can." And was thankful to be relieved by my entrance from receiving any further instructions which he knew it was useless to attempt to carry out.

" See me standin' there with a marline spike," he

said afterwards. "Bloody daft, like, that is. You can't act that way nowadays."

For one thing was certain—a regiment of soldiers with fixed bayonets would be needed to keep the trawlermen away from the enticements of that dingy waterfront, or any waterfront however uninviting, once the ropes were round the bollards. There was beer and there were tarts, attractions far too strong to be resisted. So Jim played a better card. He put them on their word. "So you won't let me down, lads, mind. Every one of you must be back aboard to-morrow morning, see?" Two older men, to whom beer still meant something but not so very much and tarts no longer anything in particular, stayed aboard to mind the ship while the rest, with hearts full of hope and eyes alight and eager for nameless adventure, trooped ashore and filled the ferry boat, a laughing cloth-capped company, jingling hard-earned change in their pockets.

"Coming ashore for a beer, Skipper?" I said.

"Well, yes. We might just go ashore and see what's doing," the Skipper said, and showed that he too was not above temptation where the lights ashore were concerned and shared with his men the same illusions.

"You goin' ashore with the Skipper?" said Sparks, and implied an unspoken invitation.

"Yes. Coming along?"

"Oh, no. I'm not the one to butt in."

"There's no butting in so far as I'm concerned."

"Well, he hasn't invited me to go with him. I'll go along with the Chief."

And he went off, exuding offended dignity and exclusiveness to find the Chief Engineer, leaving me feeling that I had committed some breach of the social code.

We left old Jake aboard to mind the ship, a tough silent old fisherman humming gently to himself, as was his habit, in the dark wheel-house.

" We shan't be gone long," the Skipper told him. " If anything's up or you want me for anything, blow two longs on the whistle. We'll hear you all right."

" Yurss," said Jake slowly. " That's right." It was his invariable reply.

The Skipper and Jim and I trooped ashore with the rest on to a wooden, sparsely lighted jetty, under the interlaced framework of the coal hoists and along a footpath that ran over hills of coal dust to a ferry. Nothing grew upon these man-made mountains and our feet crunched grittily upon the clinker pathway. It was like stepping ashore on some blasted and inhospitable wasteland, foreign and utterly un-English. The very wind smelt strange and sulphurous as though it had been belched out of the mouths of machines and did not blow from God at all.

" What a place for a murder," said one.

Blyth is a " special area." Just how very special a special area can be I had not realized until I walked up its unspeakable streets with the Skipper and Jim, they eager for some gaiety I knew the place could not possibly offer, and I aghast. I remembered having been to Swansea once when all the tin-plate works were idle. I knew some people who lived nearby. But they went blandly shootin' and golfin' and paying calls apparently unconscious, except for a faintly uncomfortable feeling of distaste, of all the misery and decay around them. They said that " of course there were no decent shops in Swansea or Cardiff and whenever they wanted to buy anything they simply had to go up to town "—meaning London, which was such a bore. So I had not really seen how special was the area I was visiting. But when I worked in the Mile End Road I used, during my lunch hour, to make excursions away from the Whitechapel High Street, where the spry Jews went with oriental pointed toes and high stuffed shoulders, into the noisy, dirty, bawdy regions behind. There was a lustiness and gusto about poverty there, about the youths who lounged against lamp-posts and spoke out of loose pendulous mouths, full of rotten teeth, a strange language devoid of consonants. There was a fine abandon about the shrieking old women who tore at each other's hair and flung abuse outside the public bars. But here in Blyth misery was shame-faced. It slunk silently round corners and went shuffling away up back alleys. It looked at you with eyes that had no expression, no emotion, no hostility even. In Glasgow, I remembered, the noisy hordes, swarming in the tenement alleys, had been like ants disturbed. You felt the draught of human emotion, hatred and rebellion and religious intolerance, blowing down the chasms of those streets. But Blyth, without complaint, without protest or rebellion, it seemed, was just decaying away, dropping to bits. It seemed incredible that this dead town, without a single softening touch of beauty, from which all hope seemed to have vanished, its streets hushed into a strange silence of decay, should be indeed England.

Rows of little two-storied houses, some of them derelict, all of them mean, ran down to a main street where little shops were, aglow with lights. Except for an occasional motor-bus no traffic passed along it. The place seemed dead and the foot-falls of the people on the pavement seemed to accentuate the hush. Every few yards there was a pub and knots of people surrounded the doors of every one. There were almost as many chapels shouting texts at you from notice-boards. As an alternative to escape through alcohol they offered vociferously escape through God.

We found it difficult, as you may imagine, to find a place of entertainment that suited the mood of the moment. The Skipper and Jim were all for "a nice bit of plush and a bit of a sit-down, like." Or a bit of music perhaps. But I myself was beginning to feel like hell so I didn't mind where I went. We came to an open square with a car-park without any cars in it. It was surrounded by pubs advertising various kinds of beer in neon signs, each with its knot of people around the public bar. There was a cinema ablaze with light (yet another escape), luring the people to enter and exchange for sixpence their drab and dingy world for the dangerous but bracing atmosphere of Chicago, the glitter of Broadway or the scorching sun of Arizona. A kind of temple, that cinema, dispensing the water of Lethe in continuous and liberal doses.

But we were not feeling like those artificial delights. We chose our haven from among the brilliant pubs.

Jim seemed to know, so we followed him with that slight thrill of expectancy which one always feels when one first enters a place full of people, and which is invariably dissipated in two minutes. Why should one always half believe that one will find a fairy godmother drinking beer in a saloon bar, a long looked-for love in a lounge, the end of life's journey in a café-bar? But having chosen our haven of delight we had a still more difficult choice to make. For in this town where, if anywhere, you would think that all men were equal, equal in poverty, equal in lack of hope, equal in their lack of the things which are commonly held to make the world a pleasant place to live in, I found that apparently extremely fine distinctions were drawn. The pubs are the meeting places of the people, their forum, and they tell one much. I was astonished to be confronted in this very special town with evidence of profound social distinctions, for in every pub there were not only the private bar, the saloon bar, the lounge, with all that those variations on the same theme entail, but also the " select room " and the " select sitting-room " and even the " select family room." There was no very obvious difference, so far as I could see, between any of these. In each some elderly ladies were sitting, sad, silent but select, with glasses of stout in front of them. So we chose the saloon bar, feeling that the atmosphere there would be more familiar. Little tables were dotted about with people sitting at them. Some young men were playing darts and talking a staccato language that was difficult to follow. All the people at the little tables were watching them in lack-lustre silence, betraying no emotion or interest in the game at all, or in each other, or in us when we entered. Up at the bar a thin shabby man was holding forth.

"Tell you what it'll be next," he was saying, "—our colonies! That's what it'll be. 'E wants Tanganyika and South-West Africa, and the Cameroons. You see! But we shan't give 'em back. Can't do. Sacred duty to the natives. And look at Japan now. She wants 'Ong-Kong. Directly there's trouble here she'll pinch it. And look at Mussolini, he's got his eye on our interests in the Mediterranean. . . ."

Who, I wondered, had an eye on our interests in Blyth?

"Well, I dunno," said the Skipper in a tone of sad disappointment and disillusion. "This doesn't seem up to much."

"There you are," I said. "The sailor ashore! Always looking for something that doesn't exist. What d'you expect to find here, anyway?"

We trooped out into the glare of the red and yellow neon signs. The stars shone faintly above it. Far off on the light wind I heard a hooter blow—two longs.

"There's Jake blowing!" I said.

"Ah, come on! That's not our hooter. We've got to see what's in this town before we go aboard!"

In a "select family sitting-room" across the square we finished up this gay enchanted evening. It was hardly what we sought, I think. A sad and silent company of shabby people gazed at us like ghosts as we entered. Near the little brass-topped table where we sat down were two lads whom I took for young miners. They were shabbily but cleanly dressed but they had no life, no fire seemed to burn within them.

They gazed at us blankly when we came in. I guessed that they were out of work. On the other side of our table was a woman with a lined face and a battered hat like a flower-pot on her head. Her hands, when she stretched them out to the glass before her, were bent and misshapen with hard work. Her eyes, like those of the two lads, were tired and somehow hopeless, but they smiled readily enough if you caught them above the glass of beer. In this bar, among these northern people, I must have seemed even more foreign than I did in Grimsby, yet there was nothing but friendliness in the eyes that looked at me from every corner of the room. Whenever I caught the eyes of the two lads they winked and nodded and grinned but never said a word, as though to attempt such a means of communication were useless. We sat for quite a long time thus, nearly until that shocking noise began which indicates in all English drinking places that you must not drink any more. We sat in silence, sometimes lifting a glass to each other and saying "Cheers!", sometimes winking or nodding silently at our neighbours.

Suddenly an old man near the fireplace broke the almost sacramental hush of the place.

"Yer bastard!" he screamed. "Gar! Yer bloody bastard!" And he bent spewing and retching into the grate.

"Nay, fayther, nay. Come away home now," a soft and utterly weary woman's voice coaxed and cajoled. "Nay now, come away home. Come away then."

"I'll not go home, nah, nah! I'll not go home. Ye're a lot of bleedin' bastards all the —in' lot of you!" Slobbering and retching he suffered himself to be led out into the night.

But on the listless silence of the rest of the company this scene had no visible effect. It moved them to no emotion. Only the two lads winked and the woman in the battered hat smiled, a tolerant indulgent smile.

"It's the hard stuff 'e's on to-night," she said. "Take my advice, lad, and never touch spirits."

The Skipper leaned across the little table and plucked at my elbow. "Wouldn't bring the Duchess of Kent in here, would you?" he said.

"Well, I don't think much of this town," he added, when we got outside. "Not much here for chaps like us, is there?"

"No, not much," I admitted.

Out in the street he went tripping along the pavement in the manner of a footballer dribbling the ball and made football passes at orange skins and cigarette packets lying in the gutter.

"Yes," said Jim reflectively. "I wouldn't mind bein' back at the little old fireside now with the kids in bed upstairs. . . ."

As we went down the street I heard a hooter blow again, two longs.

But there was a small pub up a side street which we did not visit, being too grand perhaps, or perhaps just because we did not know it existed. But the deckies knew about it. It was one of several and well known on all the ships that called for coal at Blyth. Several men in the *Lincoln Star* had been to Blyth before and they led the way. For if you got on the right side of the man that ran the place, in other words, if you spent enough of your good and hard-earned money in the bar, you could get drinks after closing time—in fact any hour of the night. Not only that but he could arrange for tarts to come round and get you fixed up for the night. There were rooms upstairs. Things were plum easy in Blyth, for prostitution is one of the accompaniments of distress in special areas. "After all," said the Bo'sn, "They must earn the money somehow."

So, not twelve hours out of Grimsby, nearly all the men found in these frowsty dives what they went ashore to find. They came back singly or in pairs by the last ferry when the sky above the gaunt derricks was filled with stars, or by the first ferry in the morning when the sun was rising beyond the river's mouth. Or later still when he had gone up above the town of Blyth and another ugly workless day was a quarter done.

"Yurss," said Jake when we got back to the ship. "I was a-blowin', but I didn't think you'd hear. There's a wire for the cook. His missus is a-dyin' it seems. Cancer of the breast or summat. They always reckoned she wouldn't last."

But the cook was ashore with his shipmates, so the wire would have to wait.

CHAPTER IV

"No, there ain't much in Blyth," said the pilot. "You're right there."

Slowly we slipped out of the river's mouth and that decaying waterfront dropped away from us.

"No, there's not much to it. Nor never likely to be from what I can see. Things are pretty bad. Well, here's my boat. Good luck to ye, Skipper, and good fishin' !"

Soon we had passed the outer buoy. We saw the backs of muddy breakers curving upon black sands, line upon line along a lonely shore. A figure crawled distantly, like an ant, along the beach. Beyond were factory chimneys from which no smoke went up. We rose and sank gently upon the swell and were at sea again.

I watched the dark autumnal shore of England recede and fade, thinking how familiar it seemed to be once more in a ship at sea. One would expect the sea to be utterly different in different parts of the world, to give a different greeting or a different farewell. Yet, however strange and foreign the land you leave, the sea is always immediately familiar. Only the great arc of sky changes but the sea, taking colour from the sky, makes always the same creaming hiss past the ship's side, the same break outwards foaming from the bows, and stretches the same, wrinkled to the very edge of the world. So when the *Lincoln Star* began to pitch lightly once again I felt less adrift than I had felt in the ghostly streets of Blyth. I began, on that account, to conjure up out of the past a strange procession of friendly memories about the sea. It seemed a good time to look back a little, and even at the risk of being utterly tiresome and boring I shall write down what I remembered, pinning down for all time these frail ghosts of mine like butterflies upon a board. For, looking back, it seems that perhaps for me also there is no escape. Though I may think the sea has not claimed me, it may be that in reality I was marked down very early and have, without knowing it, been in chains from my infancy. What otherwise could be the meaning of this strange chain of images, salient incidents standing out so clearly in my memory, each one having the sea at its core like a whelk shell held up to the ear?

My very dimmest, earliest recollection, the first dawn of my consciousness so far as I myself am now aware of it, is of the sea. It is now for me like something dreamt the night before last, forgotten all day, other dreams and thoughts and all the business of long days imposed upon it, but recalled with a conscious effort, faintly, a single isolated vision. I am suspended, apparently between heaven and earth, above a strip of shingle beach. Above me there looms something overpowering and vast, dark but shapeless, reaching up to the very sky. Suddenly from this towering bulk there breaks a hellish and horrifying noise, a cry of inextinguishable pain. Then all is dark. I know now that I was eighteen months old, crossing by steamer in my nurse's arms from Folkestone to Boulogne with my parents. We spent a month at

Ambleteuse. As my nurse was carrying me up the gangway the boat's whistle blew and terrified me. I wailed without ceasing for hours afterwards. What was the significance of the shingle beach in this picture I have never discovered. Perhaps it was superimposed upon the vision in after years. But who knows how much of what I do now, and how much of what I write here, might be ascribed to that awful noise, stabbing like a sword of terror into my infant consciousness?

At the early age of seven I went to a boarding school at Folkestone. The memory of my unhappy months there is like a nightmare to me for I had scarcely learnt not to wet my bed. There was a sadistic headmaster who used to stand me in his study in front of him and say, " What? You forgot? So you forgot, eh? How would you like to have your memory refreshed? Don't you think it would be a good idea to refresh that memory of yours just a little? Put your hand behind the cushions of that sofa. What do you feel there? A cane? I thought so. Give it to me. Now bend over, my boy. I'm going to help you not to forget." And I, aged seven, would catch hold of his hand, weeping, and beg him, aged about forty-five, to have mercy upon me and not to beat me. But always in vain. Once he hit me a terrific blow on the side of the head for not calling him " Sir," so that my face was swollen for several days. He is dead now and perhaps his soul is at this moment grilling in hell for these offences. But I'm afraid not. I remember, too, that to get to the lavatory you had to pass a long dark passage where evil

Thinking aloud.

spirits lurked, waiting to pounce upon you out of the gloom. Night after night I would wet my bed rather than go to the lavatory past this passage. And no one understood. In my misery at this place I had two comforters—the South-Eastern Railway (as it then was) and the sea. The love of trains has never left me, nor shall I ever forget the daily thrill of the ten o'clock boat train, leaving for London and home, beyond the football field. So spellbound was I, watching it out of the schoolroom window, that I earned a rap over the knuckles every day and an acid comment in my end-of-term report. " Inattentive. Does not concentrate." But at night I would lie in bed watching the shadows of branches thrown by street lamps upon the dormitory ceiling and listening to the lost and lonely sounds of ships at sea. Every few seconds a lighthouse beam swept across the sky above the house tops. On Sunday afternoons we went for a walk, a crocodile of silly little boys in round caps, shepherded by a junior master. Before we started out it was always put to the vote where we should go. A clamour of shrill voices arose in which mine could be heard piping " Oo-o-h, Sir! Down to the sea, down to the sea! Please Sir! Down to the sea! " If we went down to the sea front I forgot the small but heavy sorrows of childhood so far that now my chief memories of that preparatory school, which never prepared me for anything, are not the head-master and his cane, or the dark passage with its bogeys, but the grey lovely sea curling back on itself upon its steep stones in what I learnt was the characteristic English Channel way, the long line of Dungeness which I knew was the end of the world and, utterly thrilling and mysterious, a low far-off white line—the coast of France.

Every summer holidays we went to the sea for a month, like other children. We would arrive in the afternoon and then, after tea, my sister and I would run out together shouting, "The sea, the sea! We want to look at the sea!" When we came to it we would stand suddenly awed and silent, hand in hand, —strange little figures, she with pig-tails and I in a kilt—gazing at that vast and eternal thing with weary ships far out upon its vagueness and the ceaseless curl and whisper near at hand. One day I said, "Mummy, which is the oldest, the sea or God?"

"God, darling, of course. Don't be silly."

"There was nothing before the sea was, was there?"

"No, darling. Nothing."

"But where was God before the sea was, when there was nowhere for Him to be?"

"Run along, darling, and don't ask silly questions. Mummy's busy."

From these holidays we brought back treasures to remind us of the sea during the winter months when we were far away from it. A long frond of ribbon seaweed, perhaps, like mermaids' hair. You hung it up and it told you what the weather was to be, becoming soft when it was wet and hard when it was dry, until someone threw it away saying she couldn't think what we wanted to keep that dirty disgusting thing for. Or a smooth round pebble that had looked like a jewel when you had picked it up but now had lost all its lustre and looked like a very ordinary stone.

Or a whelk shell in which, when you held it to your ear, you could hear again the incoming tide. But we took home also—as who has not?—memories of all those sweet things which still live long after these trophies have all been lost, the larks above the gorse and the scented downs; the far blue " many twinkling laughter " of the ocean; holes in the sand that slowly fill and squelch as you dig; fishes that dart between the toes and little bladders that pop softly as you walk; the hoarse murmur of the sea at night above the voices of the people.

We used to go mackerel fishing with old Hook. This kindly bearded old fisherman is now long dead, I suppose. He owned a sailing dinghy on the south Devon coast. We would come down to the beach early in the morning, each carrying a line weighted with lead wound upon a square wooden frame.

" 'Mornin', missie and sir," old Hook would say, sitting on the gunwale of his boat, and would lift one stubby forefinger to his cap. " 'Tis a fine mornin' for you." And then he did a surprising and miraculous thing. He took off his cap, exposing to the soft breeze a polished ivory dome amid an aura of greying brown hair. From the peak of the cap he extracted tobacco, cigarette-paper and matches. He rolled himself a cigarette in his short hard fingers, lit it and stowed the whole outfit away in his cap again. Then he put his cap back on his dome and no one would guess that there was anything inside it. For me this had all the magic of a conjuring trick and never failed to leave me round-eyed and speechless with astonishment. Then we would get into the boat and he would push her out into the gentle breakers, get in himself and pull with sharp strokes of the oars, looking up at the sky and saying, " 'Tis a grand day, certainly." When we were a little way out he would run up the russet sail on the mast and the *Sally* would leap forward as though suddenly set free, the water gurgling under her bows. The sail filled and, as the *Sally* rose and fell, she became a proud Argosy dipping over the summer waves and I young Jason, clear-eyed, sailing for the Golden Fleece. The town grew small and I saw the pattern of green fields and tufted trees behind it. The red cliffs slipped past and began to take on other and less familiar shapes. There, surely, were Scylla and Charybdis and there the Pillars of Hercules. There was the hill where Cyclops dwelt, terrible with his one eye. Then indeed I was near tears because of the loveliness of my young world. I put my hands on old Hook's shoulders, jumping up and down in the boat so that he had to tell me to sit down. " Take us farther out, Hook! " I cried. " Take us farther out, beyond the horizon—miles away! "

" Ah! " old Hook would laugh. " You're a sailor, my lad, I do believe." And, taking off his cap, he performed again for my delighted gaze the miracle of the tobacco and matches.

All day we trailed our spinners over the side of the boat and shouted with joy when there came a firm tug on the line and we pulled in a barred and shining victim. Soon there was a pile of them lying in the bottom of the boat, agape and fading—a flutter of a tail now and then, a sudden wriggle, their eyes goggling, their bright glory dulling slowly. Sometimes I caught more fish than my sister and said, " Well, of course I get more fish than you because I'm bigger than you and older. And grander too. I'm the King, but you're only the Queen. I am grander, aren't I, Hook? "

But, thus appealed to, Hook, the old traitor, only laughed and said, " You'll be a fine man one day, sonnie. Go on like this and maybe you'll be a fisherman."

But sometimes my rival caught more than me so that the sun went in for me and my summer sky clouded over. There was rage in my heart, especially as she said nothing but hummed an endless song of triumph to herself as she pulled them in one after another over the gunwale into the bottom of the boat.

When we turned home the stars came out and spread a net over us. The water was like fire about the bows and ran like flame off our hands. Summer lightning flickered out to sea. The town became a bright string of lights, while here and there burnt other lights inland.

But darkness closes down over old Hook with his miraculous cap and over the proud ship he owned. Yet the shades of the prison house have not succeeded in shutting out the memory of them and it will remain fresh until I die.

I always believed, and still do, that my holiday by the sea was at least a partial failure if it did not bring at any rate one tempestuous day when I could give myself the thrill and faint terror of beholding the sea lashed into a fury. I would spend hours watching the advance and tumult of great breakers upon the rocks. Somewhere, in a drawer, there is a picture postcard depicting a magnificent confusion of surf in Cornwall. On the back of it, in my round imperfect child's hand, is written, "Just to show you when there is a bit of wind how the sea goes." I hope whoever received it realized that it was profoundly important and significant for me that the sea did indeed go like that when there was a bit of wind. It was a real discovery, a piece of headline news, that I was imparting on that postcard. My father understood the importance of this, for the boy lives in most men all their lives. Women grow up too completely and hardly recognize their childhood's ghosts when they meet them again so that they never understand. Or, if they once understood, they forget. My father and I stood often watching the furious sea, catching our breath as cold spray flew over us, dodging out of the way of each upward rush of foam, and saying "Coo! Look! Here comes a beauty!" And, when the seething climax was over, looking at each other with laughter as we shook the drops off our clothes. "That was a whopper, wasn't it?"

I have never shaken off this silly habit. I have shared the exhilaration of this furious sport with all sorts of other devotees of various nations and languages in all sorts of improbable places, always refusing to admit afterwards what I have been doing as though it were an immoral practice. I have dodged and guffawed among the polyglot crowds on Brighton front and then slunk guiltily away as though I had no business to be there. One day I was standing upon a rock on the coast of France, watching with rapt attention a splendid surf charging up the sands to boil and froth at my feet. Suddenly a voice said:

"You have better coasts than this in England, M'sieu—no?"

"Oh, no. Not at all," I said politely.

This began a friendship which lasted all the summer. It was a one-sided sort of affair for I was a cold reserved boy at sixteen and never gave anything of myself. Perhaps there was nothing much to give. Armand was a young Jesuit undergoing an arduous training for the priesthood. At present he was doing his military service and wore a horizon blue uniform. He had the alert but slightly untidy appearance that belongs to the French soldier. He told me about himself during the long walks we took together around the dusty lanes of northern France, through muddy farmyards, under the tall elms clipped like Turk's heads, and the shimmering poplars where no birds sang. We drank beer in little estaminets among peasants in their blue trousers. They sat talking rapidly to Madame, in her slippers and dirty blouse, and took no notice of us at all, as is usual in France, but went on with their incomprehensible talk. Armand must have found me dull enough for I never opened out to him at all so far as I remember and when we parted at the end of the summer, having seen each other almost every day, he must have known as little about his strange shy English companion as when we first met on the rocks watching the sea.

One day Armand pointed to a huge legend which

stands marked out in chalk upon the bare downs near Boulogne—" *Gloire à Jésus Christ.*"

" One must know what one wishes to do," he said. " You see that? That is my life." He opened the collar of his tunic and showed me a silver cross at his throat. " To-morrow I go back to Paris. Soon I put on another soldier's uniform. I join another army. Remember, I am always your boy."

He gave me his hand and I never saw or heard of him again. By now very many others besides myself are doubtless the better because Armand had found what he wished to do.

There are so many other memories of the sea, most of them unimportant, some of them pleasant and full of beauty. Others painful, even to tears, the hot furious tears of youth. To recount them all would be weariness to the flesh for they matter to no one but me. And then there are all those years in the south when the sea was an ever-present power that filled my life. And so, when the dark land of England fell away astern again and the *Lincoln Star* began to lift upon the swell, I stood upon the main-deck and, resting my elbows upon the rail, bent over towards the foam that raced frothing below me.

" How now, old friend and enemy? " I said.

The day after leaving Blyth we passed the Orkneys which were long, low, dark bars upon the west. Gannets swooped around and fell like plummets into the water. Fair Isle fell away upon our starboard quarter, remote and lonely with a skirt of foam. And the next day we passed the Faroes which raised high, proud summits into the clouds enclosing valleys shot with light.

My world narrowed down to the compass of the little wheel-house, the chart-room behind it where the Skipper pricked off the course with dividers on a much-scored chart, the radio-room where Sparks sat all day before his complicated apparatus, the Skipper's mahogany cabin below, and the lavatory with the pump that leaked and the pedestal that did not work. Three times a day at mealtimes this tiny world enlarged just a little to include the saloon aft where we ate. The people that inhabited this microcosm became in a few days more intimately known to me than they could have become during many years in the wide world ashore.

The Skipper began to lose his dapper appearance. Motor-cars and insurance policies seemed less appropriate, for round his cheerful face a reddish iridescence began to form. A jersey of many colours, like Joseph's coat, replaced the smart suit which hung now from a coat hanger in his wardrobe like the corpse of another life. At the wheel there was usually Jim or the Bo'sn or one of the deck-hands. They wore high-necked jumpers and fear-nought trousers over which they pulled long thick sea-boot stockings. They wore slippers when not working on deck or rubber sea-boots cut right down to the ankles. Sparks lived in a blue jersey and dungaree overalls. His long black hair, less carefully brushed than formerly, fell forward over his forehead. He was continually throwing it back with a jerk of his head.

The conversation of these kindly simple people

soon became exceedingly familiar, even at times to the point of being tedious. Other trawler skippers, other mates and other deck-hands in other ships, who made the same unending journeys back and forth across these seas, were dissected and their characters laid bare over and over again and hour after hour. Old and, one knew, well-worn stories that were almost legends were brought into the light of day and savoured yet once more like chewing-gum re-chewed. This was not for my edification but for their own, stories told for the joy of telling, since I was a ghost at these recitals and stood by, listening but taking no part. And yet I did feel that I played a rôle of some sort in this talk, for continually these stories would be addressed to me or at me about people and things I had never known, was never likely to know and which could not really possibly concern me at all. Again, they were thinking aloud. I was a kind of vehicle for their thoughts, a vessel into which they poured them.

" Proper rum 'un, 'e is. Know what he did in Hammerfest? Got 'old of a car somewhere, picked up a tart and took 'er out into the country for a bit of a ride like. When 'e got back there was this tart's bloke waitin' fer 'im with a length o' pipe-line. Great bastard about seven feet high, 'e was. So d'you know what 'e done? Dropped the tart and drove out into the country and rowed back to the ship after dark, see, so the bloke never knew. What happened to the boat 'e pinched to do it I never 'eard. . . ."

But these anecdotes ran away out of the innumerable leaking cracks in the unworthy vessel they had chosen to receive them. And Jim would run on interminably, leaning upon the spokes of the steering-wheel.

"Not that I'm much of a one for late nights meself, like. Since I've been married I'd sooner stay at home of an evening, see. Still I will confess I stayed out all one night since I've been tied up. Last year it was, matter of fact. It came about this way. . . ."

And quite a large part of the talk in this tiny parliament was inevitably in a grosser vein than this. We amused ourselves with smut. And why not? Frequently, indeed, it was of an exceedingly physical kind. But there was one standing joke which never failed in its effect whenever, poor weary and dilapidated thing, it was brought, complaining slightly, out of its burrow. It seemed that a certain wireless operator in another ship, whom both the Skipper and Sparks knew, was by way of being a bit of a pansy. So they would imitate what they conceived to be his walk, one hand on swaying hip and the other held delicately aloft, up and down in the narrow space of the wheel-house. This was accompanied by endless talk in a lisping effeminate voice with the tongue held against the teeth. To me this always seemed rather a poor joke for I have never been able to see anything funny in effeminate men or masculine women any more than in blindness or deafness or any other human infirmity, nor could I imagine that anyone could really behave like that, certainly not a wireless operator in a trawler. However, for the Skipper and for Sparks it was so funny that these pantomimes always ended in their becoming doubled up with uncontrollable laughter, the Skipper slapping his thighs and Sparks throwing back his head and saying, "Oh, blimey! Oh, bloody 'ell! Strike me!" And I listened with a glassy grin.

But when the Bo'sn was present the conversation took a challenging turn and became a combat. For he threw down loud assertions that exploded among us like bombs. He was a huge man who rolled cigarettes continually and spat tobacco as he talked. Everything he said he shouted, as though to drown contradiction. Every statement he made was a challenge. At first I found it difficult to understand what he said for he spoke at a great speed and interpolated expletives beginning with the letters B and F between every third and fourth word in every sentence. This made his remarks sound almost as though they were in another language than English. It was a form of inarticulateness common to all on board, as it is, indeed, to almost all the working people of our country who seem to find their native language insufficient to express what they wish to say. Or perhaps it is just a habit, for I noticed that at first, when they did not know me well, they would talk to me without the use of these expletives but later, when they became more used to my presence, they decorated their remarks to me as freely with these embellishments as they did all that they said to one another. So every bit of the dialogue that I set down here, or most of it, must be interlarded in your imagination with words which you will seek in vain in many dictionaries, even though they are the commonest in the English language.

But the Bo'sn used these words to season his discourse more than any one else on board. I must have seemed extremely dumb to him at first for I had to translate everything he said to me in my head before I answered. Most of his remarks were like challenges to single-handed combat. If the gage were not immediately taken up he threw it down again with a still greater clatter. However, I presently grew accustomed to his particular form of intercourse and, finding that the lightning was not unloosed when I took up the challenge, I began to beat him at his own game.

" If we don't get more fish than this we'll have to sell the ship! "

If I made no answer in particular, not thinking the remark required one, it would be repeated, a bit louder this time.

" I said, if we don't get more fish than this we'll have to sell the ship! "

" Can't do that."

" 'Course we bloody well can. Skipper can sell 'er. Easy enough!"

" Criminal offence, that. Bottomry or barratry or something."

" B——. I've seen it done afore now. Ship and her whole catch sold. Whole f—— catch!"

" You get a long spell in the calaboose for that! "

" You don't know what you're f—— well talking about, you don't."

" Of course I don't. Nor do you."

Which would, of course, be the end of the engagement, the Bo'sn laughing and rolling another cigarette as he leaned on the spokes of the wheel. Or else it would be the signal for the beginning of one of those long, long stories which went to show that some one was a rum 'un and no mistake and in which the

Bo'sn and his shipmates wandered off again on thought-trails of their own, leaving me stranded, waiting for their return from the dim misty regions of reminiscence.

But the Bo'sn was a fine and likeable character full of loud laughter and kindness. He was a sort of rude, rough, jockeying father confessor to all the men on board. He heard and understood their troubles, which were simple enough, and passed loud judgment upon them. Most of us heard of the troubles and everyone heard the judgment for there was no secrecy in that little community and nothing was kept private. It was no use having secret troubles on the Iceland banks. But there was nothing, I think, that the Bo'sn did not know and understand about the uncomplicated ills that afflict fishermen in small ships. The momentary flares of anger that came when working the trawl on a filthy night, the sudden quarrels because of something imagined to have been said or done, the fancied grievance, the imagined slight, work not fully shared or time not properly apportioned—all these he could deal with in the same abrupt, authoritative, challenging way. There was no anger in his dealings with the men who worked with him and behind the hectoring manner there was a geniality which burst forth frequently in gusts of tremendous laughter, legs wide apart like a Colossus, rolling a cigarette. In the evils that came upon the fishermen from their sorry adventures ashore, the aftermaths of drink and of what did service for love, he showed an understanding that comes from long experience.

Glancing up from time to time at the compass in the deck head.

On the whole, however, there was not a great deal of talking done in the little wheel-house and much of the time was passed in silence, the helmsman smoking quietly at the wheel, glancing up from time to time at the compass in the deck head. The Skipper hummed endlessly to himself and I leaned upon the window rail gazing at the lift and fall of the bows and at the white skirts of foam that broke away from them. There is something hypnotic in that sight. It robs the mind of thought and empties it so that hours went by during which there was no sound among us but the swish of the sea and the rhythmic creak of bulkheads.

Whenever a fresh hand took over the wheel the man who gave it up would collect from the rack below the window the four or five thick blue and white mugs and take them aft to the galley. Presently he would bring them back again filled with that strange sickly brown liquid which, in small ships, passes for tea. And sometimes, feeling a sudden urge to activity, the Skipper would hop around the wheel-house with a screw of paper or an orange at his feet, going through the dancing movements of a footballer. And I would lash out with my long shanks in a mock tackle until the orange split against the wooden bulkheads, or the screw of paper fell to bits, or until I just got fed up and said:

"Oh hell! Have it your own way!"

And on the fourth day the jagged mountains of Iceland stood along the north-western horizon, their sculptured peaks slashed with a few last bars of snow.

CHAPTER V

WHEN Sergeant Edward Mace, late of the Durham Light Infantry, heard when he came aboard, after his night ashore in Blyth, that his wife was dying of cancer of the breast, he shook his head.

"Ah," he said, "I told 'er. I told 'er she ought to have something done. But no, she says, if I'm to die I'll die, and I won't have no doctors muckin' about with me. Ah well, mucked it up proper, that 'as. Now I'll have to get a new old woman."

But, in actual fact, Mrs. Mace was afraid. She had been afraid for years. She was not in the least afraid of dying, for life hadn't been such fun as all that. She was afraid of the cold, efficient, machine-like air of a hospital, of starched sisters, of bright metallic things that looked as though they would hurt, of the smell of anaesthetics, and of being "Case No. 192—Carcinoma of the left breast." When the doctor had seen her some weeks ago he had taken the Sergeant aside and said, "Look here, Mace. You'll have to have something done. I can arrange for her to go into hospital to-day." And the Sergeant shook his head, but his wife said nothing. For years she had seen this coming, this moment when she would be no longer Mrs. Ruby Mace, wife of Sergeant Edward Mace late of the Durham Light Infantry, but No. 192. So when presently a slip came from the hospital requesting her to attend for immediate attention, she turned over in her bed and faced the wall. Such fatalism or fear, I believe, is common among the poor. Now, when her husband was away at sea, she was dying. The Sergeant would probably never see her again. "That's mucked it up," he said. "Good old pal she was an' all. New old woman for me, that's what that means."

For the true love and home of Sergeant Mace was a little kingdom of pots and pans that lay aft of the engine-room of the *Lincoln Star* on the main deck. You might have seen him in it any day at sea, bending over his square coal stove, stirring a great pot of soup with an immense long spoon, or rolling out pastry on a board with flour up to his elbows. As he did these things he dripped sweat from his shining forehead into the soup, or on to the pastry board, or on to the stove where the drops sizzled and disappeared. He steadied himself with one hand by means of a rail beside the stove. Whenever the ship gave a more than usually violent plunge he shouted:

"Garn, yer muckin' bastard!" and a great deal more besides which it would be useless for me to write down since it wouldn't be printed.

On the deck of the galley there stood always a huge tea kettle which was kept permanently filled with a liquid called tea. It bore no resemblance to any tea that I have ever drunk elsewhere. It was sugared to a sickening sweetness and was made by a simple but effective process. A black dusty heap of leaves was placed in the kettle, cold water was added and an amount, not stipulated, of condensed milk. This was heated to boiling on the galley stove and an avalanche of sugar was shot into it. The mixture that resulted was in incessant demand. By all the rules I have ever been taught all our teeth should have dropped out long ago and our throats have become coated thick with tannin. But fishermen are pretty tough and every man, no matter what job he was engaged upon and no matter at what hour of the day or night, always had a mug of this concoction within reach of his hand. Alcohol of any sort is now forbidden in all trawlers. Not even a weekly tot of rum is allowed, for no way was ever found of insuring that all the rum provided for the entire trip should not be consumed within a few hours of leaving port. Since such liberality was liable to endanger ships the insurance companies now insist that no liquor shall be carried at all. So the huge friendly kettle on the galley deck with its sickening but apparently life-giving contents has taken the place of the rum jar and has, incidentally, turned the galley into a cheerful rendezvous, a place for backchat and discussion, presided over by the Sergeant in his singlet and drill trousers.

A row of china mugs hung on hooks from a shelf in the galley. Every now and then throughout the day, and throughout the night also, the men came into the galley to replenish their mugs from the kettle, or to take one down from its hook and fill it. I used to go into the galley and fill myself a mug from the kettle whenever I felt inclined, not because I felt a craving for the thick brown medicine but because I liked the comfortable glow of the galley fire and because the place was the friendliest in the ship. And because I enjoyed seeing the Sergeant bend down and open his

"Nice cup o' tea." Fishermen are pretty tough.

oven door, pulling out rows of things on a metal tray, brown, crisp and warm, his delightful handiwork.

" Nice cup o' tea," the Sergeant would say, straightening himself from the stove. " That's what you want this weather. Nice hot cup o' tea."

He was a tall thin man with almost cadaverous features. Under his cook's cap a permanently wet forelock hung down over a brow which glistened with sweat and was streaked with smudges from frequent applications of an unsavoury sweat-cloth round his neck. But his face was given military distinction by a pair of waxed moustaches, the angle of whose points seemed to betray his mood. They pointed up when his spirits rose and down when they fell. They always pointed up when he was cooking, especially when he was constructing the superb work of art with which he confronted us at tea time every Saturday, a white and pink iced cake of terrifying appearance, decorated with silver balls and peppered with cokernut. This he placed before us with a sacramental air and covered with a sheet of cellophane to keep off the flies which lived and had their being in enormous numbers in the saloon where we ate. When at work constructing these masterpieces, which lasted throughout the week, he wore an unbuttoned woollen vest, or a singlet, and a pair of drill trousers, also always unbuttoned where they ought particularly to be buttoned up. A ship under full canvas sailed proudly across his scrawny chest. Round his thin right arm snakes were entwined and the Union Jack was crossed with the Stars and Stripes upon his left. But on Saturday he changed his week-old vest and put on a clean one. He put on a clean white cook's coat and cap. For Saturday was something of a high day. On Friday afternoon the thought of the wedding-cake that he would build on the morrow began to work him up into a state of suppressed excitement. "Saturday to-morrow," he would say. "Lash yer up with a bit o' weddin' cake, Saturday. You wait—nice bit o' weddin' cake to-morrow." The art of creation went to his head like wine. When the masterpiece was finally on the saloon table before us he would thrust a skewer or a knife into his belt, mark time and about turn in the narrow swaying space of the saloon or galley. "Left! Left! Left-right-left! Er-bout turn! One, two, three, four! Pick 'em up there! Pick 'em up!" Finally he would whip the skewer out of his belt, fix an imaginary bayonet with a fine flourish and salute to the roll of drums that still echoed in his head after twenty years.

"Sergeant Edward Mace. Aye! That's me."

The Sergeant held an esteemed and respected position in the little world we lived in. For he was a first-class cook and nothing makes so much for the happiness of everyone in a small ship as good grub. Bad grub, on the other hand, is a kind of menace that hangs like a dark cloud over a little ship. It makes bad blood. It disrupts, and if you seek diligently for causes behind very numerous and diverse effects you will often find that bad grub lies at the root of the matter. So the cook more than anyone else on board can determine the happiness or otherwise of the crew during the trip. The Sergeant, however, provided good grub in plenty. At every meal the tables groaned under plates and pans and dishes of food piled layer upon layer on one another in a rich and grubby profusion. So that every man on board, except one, thought that he was exceptionally lucky to be making a trip in a ship with Sergeant Mace as cook. When the news came that Mrs. Mace was dying, all except one were filled with apprehension lest it should be necessary for the Sergeant to sign off and go home to attend to her.

" Hope we don't lose 'im. Can't afford to lose 'im, you know. Good cook, 'e is."

There was a distinct feeling of resentment against Mrs. Mace for dying thus inopportunely of cancer of the breast. She ought to be more considerate.

The galley boy, however, was suddenly unusually cheerful and was heard whistling in the galley. But he said nothing.

There was general relief when the Sergeant came aboard that morning, shook his head and said, " That's mucked it! Now I'll have to get a new old woman," and so saying exchanged his smart brown suit for the familiar singlet and drill trousers.

Two days out at sea, drinking a mug of whatever you may call it in the galley, I first noticed the Sergeant's hands. The fingers were permanently bent and shrivelled. Some of them had the end joints missing and were sad, useless stumps.

" How did you lose your finger joints? "

" Ah, bleedin' awful. Awful, it was, I tell yer." And he bent over his pot again, stirring and shaking his head and saying " Bleedin' awful. Terrible. Proper terrible, it was."

He was so inarticulate that I had to piece the story together from what others told me.

It was in Faxa Bay on the south-west coast of Iceland, in which is the capital, Reykjavik. The bay is seventy miles wide. Sudden gales sweep down from the mountains and often whip the sea into an instant fury. Off the headland that flanks the bay to the southward are the Blinders, lying in wait. Their needle tops are submerged so that the sea breaks and boils about them in savage turmoil. One winter's night the trawler *Dominican* was running for Reykjavik before a seventy-mile-an-hour south-easterly gale when, in the seething darkness, she struck the Blinders with a rending crash. Badly holed in the fish-room, and leaking in the engine-room also, she swung and bumped with every wave that swept her. At every moment the danger increased that her engine-room would be flooded and the boilers would burst. No help could come to her on such a night. So the whole crew took to the life-boat and were at sea continuously for twenty-seven hours in that icy tumult trying to make the coast some ten miles off but driven by the wind ever farther across the bay. Sergeant Mace was one of them, an old army coat over his singlet and drill trousers. It was so cold that their hands stuck to the oars, and when each man tried to leave his oar at the end of his spell to hand over to his relief, he found his fingers dead, numb, frozen in the attitude of toil to the oar he held and unable to leave go. One by one they began to fall forward over their oars, helpless with exhaustion, doped with cold. Whenever that happened the mate hit them about the shoulders and over the head, buffeting them into activity, knowing that if any man fell asleep he would never wake up. One of them did fall asleep in spite of all the mate could do for him and did not wake up. No amount of hitting and buffeting and joking kept his spirits up and he lay down in the bottom of the boat and died, his eyes quite covered over with a film of ice. But it wasn't Sergeant Mace. He took his turn with the oars and did his share of hitting and buffeting. He put on his military act to keep them alive, rattling a tattoo continuously, when he was not pulling, on the gunwales of the boat with the handles of two sheath knives. But later when his hands stuck to the oars he could not do that any more. They were picked up finally on a deserted beach in Faxa Bay by a shore rescue party. All were at the last gasp of exhaustion and the Sergeant lost the end joints of several fingers from frost bite. But all he could say of that grim nightmare adventure was:

"Awful! Ah, awful, it was. Bleedin' terrible. Terrible. Twenty-seven hours. Died, 'e did. Second Engineer—a goner. Couldn't do nothin' for 'im. Rubbed his eyes with rum to keep them from freezin' over. No good. Died, finished. Lost me fingers that way. That's how I lost me fingers. Terrible it was." And he shook his head as he bent towards the oven to pull out rows of brown shining things upon a metal tray.

The Sergeant's right-hand man, Prime Minister and Grand Vizier in his little hot swaying empire of pots and pans, was a lad of sixteen. He was also what is known as a "deckie-learner," an apprentice deck-hand, learning the job. So when we got to the banks and fishing began in earnest he relinquished his office of Prime Minister and went to work on deck. He put off his uniform of state, which consisted of a torn shirt and a pair of dungaree trousers, and put on the jersey and thigh boots that the deck-hands wore. One gathered that he laid down the burden of office without any particular regret. Not that his duties were very arduous but the Sergeant's rule was no light one. For when he felt disposed, and when the points of his moustache tended to droop, the Sergeant poured out the vials of his wrath upon the head of his faithful minister and only subject. This he did in old-fashioned army style and continued to do so sometimes from the moment the boy lit the galley fire in the morning until he had washed the tea things and emptied the galley buckets last thing at night. The fact that the boy was a half-caste made this easy. To the rest of the men he was known affectionately as Jack Johnson. To his immediate superior he was known by an infinite variety of delightful and descriptive names.

Jack Johnson took this rather ill though he said nothing. He was sensitive about his dark complexion and took refuge behind a somewhat hang-dog sullenness and an air of suspicion which he wore like a kind of armour. It was a long time before any chink could be found in it. He was extremely doubtful about me for weeks and, until near the end of the voyage, had nothing for me but a dark and glittering stare. I would feel it being directed upon me from a great way off. As I sat at the saloon table eating I

It robs the mind of thought.

would feel it and, looking up, would see Jack Johnson in the pantry gazing at me with his sullen dark eyes while he slowly wiped a plate with a cloth. Sometimes, when I was standing in the galley with a mug of tea talking to the Sergeant, I would become suddenly aware of the boy's eyes burning into me as he sat peeling potatoes on a stool. I wondered whether, perhaps, some strange ancient hostility smouldered in his dark blood, some fire that he himself felt but could not perceive, something that reached back into time and had no relation to me at all, or to this ship, or to the little galley where he worked, but came from his savage ancestors who had danced long ago in a jungle kraal in tropic Africa, wore feathers in their heads and spun screaming round and round, gashing themselves with knives, until they dropped from exhaustion upon the ground. Perhaps on the other hand, I reflected, and more probably, he was only a little thick in the head.

However, I did eventually find a chink in the armour. It is extraordinary how these things happen. There are, particularly at certain seasons, in the seas round Iceland, enormous jelly fish whose presence is held by the fishermen to be a sign of poor fishing. When these jelly fish are abundant, they predict, the fish will be found to be scarce. Often these huge frail scalloped creatures go pulsing past in hundreds, deep in the cold gloom, trailing webs of long stinging threads behind them with which they ensnare the tiny creatures they feed upon. The fishermen hate these jelly fish, not only because they indicate bad fishing but because their threads sting the hands and bring the skin up in a rash. They call them "sluthers."

One day in the saloon I said to the mate, airing my newly-acquired knowledge, "Hell of a lot of sluggers around here, Jim!"

A little knowledge, I found, is a dangerous thing. Jack Johnson, who was collecting plates from the table, dropped them with a clatter at my mispronunciation of this familiar word and fled into the pantry where I heard him giving rein to his indecent laughter. But thereafter the glittering and hostile stare ceased, for Jack Johnson came to the conclusion, I suppose, that I was a thing of human frailties after all.

Jack Johnson had a large number of humble but necessary duties to perform. He washed pots, pans and dishes in a greasy brown stew in the pantry. He scrubbed down the deck of the saloon and of the deckies' mess that led off it. He peeled potatoes and emptied the galley buckets over the lee rail. He kneaded the dough for the bread the Sergeant made twice a week. He was driven to all these tasks by the whip-lash of the Sergeant's tongue which he bore in sullen resentful silence. In the same silence he worked. You could see him punching and pummelling dough in the pantry as though it was the Sergeant himself he was belabouring.

For some reason it was ordained by the Sergeant that the kettle which stood on the galley deck, filled with its brown mixture, was a sacred and forbidden object. He placed a taboo upon it. It might be tended only by himself. Only his hand might heap in it the mingled tea leaves and condensed milk or pour on to the heap the water from another kettle which always stood on the galley stove, making it send up its cloying vapour. And, above all, only he might decide whether a new mixture should be made or more hot water added to the old brew. I never could discover the reason for this unwritten but inviolable law. Whenever I was bold enough to ask the Sergeant he only shook his head and said, "Ah, I look after that. Look after the tea, always have done." And I was not any more exempt from this rule than anyone else and when, on one occasion, I lifted the lid of the kettle to fill it with hot water from the other that stood sizzling on the stove, the Sergeant made a dive across the galley, took the kettle from me and filled it himself. With his baleful eyes Jack Johnson watched, over a bucket of potato peelings, my ignominious retreat.

In the wheel-house there was a rack with four compartments. It held four mugs, one for the Skipper or the Mate, one for the man at the wheel, one for Sparks and a spare one. During this trip the spare one was occupied by a mug for me though I never did anything to deserve such a privilege. These mugs were never allowed to remain empty for very long. Every so often one of the deckies would come up on the bridge.

"Pot o' tea, Skipper?"

"Eh? Yes, please, Jake."

"Sparks? Pot o' tea?"

"Aye. Don't mind if I do."

And then to me, "What about you? Want another?"

"Well, I've only just had one, you know."

" Ah well, another won't do you no harm."

And away Jake would go with his four mugs all gripped in a bunch by the handles, white with blue bands, chipped round the edges and smeared with black thumb marks, all together in his horny fist. I always sensed the special friendliness of these offers. They meant more than just fetching me a mug of tea and so, because I did not like to refuse, I consumed pints of tea that I did not know how to put away. More than once, I am afraid, I secretly and surreptitiously emptied them into the sea.

But later on in the trip I began to do these small services myself and would take the empty mugs from their rack on the bridge.

" More tea, Jim ? "

" Ah well, if you're going that way, Dick. Always ready for drop o' tea."

Then I would carry the mugs, all together by their handles, down the companion to the deck (a considerable feat this!) and along the deck to the galley where the Sergeant was busy over his stove.

" Any tea in the kettle, old soldier? "

" Aye. Nice cup o' tea, I made yer. That's what yer want this weather. Nice cup o' tea."

And carefully, almost reverently, he would lift the lid of the kettle and peer in to see that it was full. Then I would carry the bunch of mugs back again, spilling their brown contents as I went, along the deck and up the companion again (a still more considerable feat!) and place them in the wheel-house rack, feeling that I had rendered a service. As, indeed, I had.

"There you are, Jim."

"Ah, thanks, Dick. Thank you kindly."

Sometimes, when there was a pause in the galley, the thought of the row of mugs, possibly empty, in the wheel-house would occur to the Sergeant himself and he would, it seemed, be overcome by an irresistible desire to replenish them with his own hand. Then he would leave the galley and go up on the bridge. This usually happened about eleven o'clock in the morning but it also happened when the day's work was over about eight o'clock in the evening before he settled down to his game of solo whist. When he paid these visits to the wheel-house you could almost tell by his manner what day of the week it was. On Monday or Tuesday he would stand and gaze through the wheel-house windows at the rise and fall of the bows and the arcs of foam that broke out from them, shake his head and say, "Ah!" On Wednesday or Thursday he would concede to the world a little more than that and say, "Ah! Bleedin' awful weather. Bloody terrible!" or else, "Nice drop o' weather, this. Keeps on like this we'll be all right." But on Friday there would be a kind of excitement in his manner. The points of his moustache would be looking upwards and he would say, "Saturday to-morrow! Lash yer up with a bit o' weddin' cake, Saturday!" And on Saturday itself he would be a changed man with a new white coat and apron on and perhaps a white cook's cap. His moustaches were waxed and pointed proudly heavenward. There was almost a kind of exaltation in his manner, for on that day there would be fashioned under those skilled but pitiful fingers, from which the joints were missing, yet another masterpiece in white, blue, vermilion and silver, fashioned and born out of the hot savoury womb of the Sergeant's oven. On Saturdays, therefore, he strutted and about-turned and fixed bayonets in the little wheel-house, performing a kind of war dance inspired by the fever and fury of the culinary afflatus.

So it was particularly unfortunate that the incident I am about to relate should have occurred on no other day than on Saturday itself, the sixth day that he had blessed and hallowed. It was my fault, I suppose. I should never have made friends with the Sergeant's Prime Minister, a base act of treason in any case. However I could not help it for, ever since my gaff about the " sluthers," Jack Johnson had been getting friendlier and friendlier. He knew no way of expressing his sudden change of opinion about me other than by grinning with discoloured teeth, instead of glowering, and—disconcertingly enough—by pressing upon me even more mugs of tea until I thought I should drown in it. I meant no treason against the Sergeant by accepting these overtures in the spirit in which they were offered, even though most of the tea that inevitably accompanied them went over the side. But the situation presently became beyond my control for, on one occasion, in his eagerness to make me a brown and sickly oversweetened peace offering Jack Johnson committed an unpardonable offence, a shocking and sacrilegious act. He interfered with the kettle.

One Saturday evening after tea I was standing in the wheel-house. Jim was at the wheel and the Skipper, his elbows on the rail that ran beneath the window, was keeping up a continuous refrain composed of snatches of current popular songs—a somewhat unfortunate habit of his. I had been obliged, under the Sergeant's eye, to get round a large slice of his latest and finest creation and had not yet quite recovered from the choking sensation that cake always produces in me, even the lightest and most delicate cake. The Sergeant's nearly suffocated me. Jack Johnson put his swarthy head in at the door.

" 'Ere! " he said, beckoning me outside with a conspiratorial backward jerk of his head. " Like another pot o' tea? I can get you one if you like."

I had not the heart to refuse. No captain of industry was ever offered a title with an air of greater import. Coronets and portfolios changed hands in that confidential and covert manner. Secret treaties and alliances were made thus. So I felt it was far more than a cup of sickly tea that I was accepting. It was a crown, a palm, a secret bond. How was I to guess what dreadful act of sacrilege was being conceived in his dark brain?

So I said, " Thanks, son. I don't mind." One could always empty it over the side presently when he wasn't looking.

When he came into the wheel-house a little later and handed the mug to me with a black thumb-nail above the rim, he said with an air of illicit triumph:

" I got it for yer all right."

I should have guessed then, but of course I did not. I placed the mug in the rack, awaiting an opportunity to throw its hot cloying contents away.

But the Sergeant, in the middle of his game of solo whist in the saloon, had heard unaccustomed sounds in the galley above. He put down his cards and went, silently as a footpad, up the companion ladder that led from the deckies' mess to the galley. There, red-handed, he caught Jack Johnson in the very act of heaping new tea leaves into the kettle. What greater outrage could be committed under his eyes?

"What the bleedin' 'ell d'you think yer playin' at?"

"Makin' some more tea, o' course. What d'yer think?"

"Who told you to make more tea?"

"No b——. The bloke up there ain't got none."

"I'll muckin' soon show you who ain't got none."

But the boy went on, darkly and sullenly, with his felonious business, his horrid act of lèse majesté. He lifted the kettle with its new heap of tea leaves and sugar in it and filled it deliberately and slowly from the kettle on the galley stove. Then the Sergeant let loose a terrifying spate of fury upon the head of his subordinate, harking back to do so to his army days of twenty years ago. He threw doubts on the parentage of Jack Johnson and stated that he had been begotten in one of several bizarre and irregular ways. And born under circumstances hardly less abnormal. He inferred that the boy himself was addicted to all sorts of curious and interesting practices. But the boy said nothing. His eye dark and burning, he slowly filled my mug and left the galley with it. The Sergeant followed him along the deck in a paroxysm of soldierly fury which we, in the wheel-house on the bridge, could hear approaching above the swish of the bow wave. That was why the boy was a bit breathless when he reached the wheel-house with my mug of tea. He said, " I got it for yer, all right! " and then stood his ground defiantly, his dark eyes savage.

The Sergeant burst in upon us. His moustache bristled with rage. Beads of sweat stood upon his outraged brow.

" I'll teach yer to interfere with my business, yer missionary eatin' Zulu! " He turned to the Skipper. " Interferin' with my muckin' kettle, 'e was! " He was choking with fury. " Caught 'im at it. 'E knows, 'e does, no one makes the muckin' tea but me. I'll teach yer, yer son of a Parsee bitch! " And he made a furious lunge at the boy who dodged and fled out of the door. The Sergeant rushed out, white hot with fury, to follow up his attack.

" You'd better see to the cook. 'E's out." The boy put his head in at the wheel-house door. There was a dark glitter of triumph in his eye.

On the main-deck the Sergeant lay with his head in the scuppers. He was moaning a little. A trickle of blood ran from his hair across his temple. There was blood on his moustache, oozing from his upper lip. He lay on his side, his legs scissor-wise across the deck.

We lifted him, and, supporting him with difficulty between us, got him up to the wheel-house and down the companion to the Skipper's cabin. There we stretched him out painfully on the settee. We bathed his not very serious wounds.

" Have a fag, old soldier," I said.

" Ah," said the wounded soldier. " Ah. Terrible. Bleedin' terrible! "

He lay and moaned for a bit, pressing his hand to his back and complaining of indefinable pains.

" You take a rest, old chap," I said, and left him. I refrained carefully from any inquiry as to what had happened.

" Yurss," said Jake, leaning on the spokes of the wheel. " I see'd it comin' to 'im. Serve 'im right."

When I went down half-an-hour later to see how the Sergeant was getting on, he was smoking another cigarette. When I entered he pressed his hand to his back and moaned again.

" Must have slipped, that's what," he said. " Slipped and caught me head on the rail. Bleedin' terrible, broken me back I wouldn't be surprised."

" That's right. You just slipped I expect. You'll be all right."

" Ay. Reckon that's it. Slipped and hit me head on the rail. That's what it was. Bleedin' dangerous, them decks."

" Have a cigarette."

" Ah! Slipped, that's what it was."

And he had persuaded himself that it was so. He lay for a long while, two hours or more, smoking and moaning, a soldier wounded by stealth, ambushed. Presently he got up and began stiffly, one hand on the small of his back and the other supporting him on the edge of the table, to move slowly round the cabin. I undressed and got into the Skipper's bunk where I was sleeping while fishing was on. It was past midnight when the Sergeant said:

" He ain't no good, that bloody boy. No good, 'e ain't. Young bastard."

" Oh, forget it, old soldier," I said. " You just slipped, that's all."

But in the boy's dark eye there shone a new and unaccustomed fire, the light of victory.

" Look out! " said the men to one another next day. " Here comes the Basher! "

" I got it for yer all right, didn't I? " he said.

CHAPTER VI

" DINNER—oh! "

The Sergeant had a police whistle with which he made a shrill scream up the speaking-tube from the engine-room to the bridge. Those on the bridge knew, when they heard that high bat-like sound at noon, that yet another meal was ready in the saloon aft or in the deckies' mess that adjoined it.

It squeaked three times a day, this imperious summons, at seven for breakfast, at noon for dinner and at six for tea. I seldom heard it squeak at seven, or if I did I ignored it, because at that hour, after a night on the chart-room settee or—when we were fishing—in the Skipper's cabin, I could not face the huge piles of rubbery-looking fat bacon, swimming in a brown juice full of greasy globules, which the Sergeant provided as an overture to each day at sea. I sustained myself until noon with mugs of tea instead. But at " Dinner—oh! " I was glad to hear the squeak in the speaking-tube. I was glad at " Tea—oh! " too, not because I was particularly hungry at that hour but because the fuggy friendliness of the saloon was a pleasant thing in the evening, and because the half-hour or so when we sat over yet another mug of tea after every meal was a genial and heartening interval in the day. I learnt more about my companions during that time than at any other.

The first time I heard the admonitory squeak in the wheel-house I went aft and down the companion ladder and seated myself at the table in the deckies' mess.

"You can go in the cabin, you can," said the Sergeant with the air of the host, saying, "Friend, go up higher." By this he meant that I was privileged to eat with the Skipper, the Mate, Sparks and the Chief Engineer in the small mahogany-panelled saloon adjoining. So I got up and went there. But I found that my presence immediately created a problem, for the table, and the settee that ran along the bulkheads on three sides of it, had room for four people only. This meant that while I ate one of the others must wait. Or else I must wait while they ate. As it happened, this difficult problem usually solved itself for it was seldom that all of us were present at the same time. But when this occurred it was always Sparks who gave way, laughing and saying, "Oh, bloody 'ell! No room for me, I can see that!" And all my offers to wait until there was room for me were indignantly refused.

The saloon where we ate was the Sergeant's particular pride. He had given full rein there to his artistic genius. He had expressed himself by adding a number of characteristic touches to the somewhat austere appearance of the tiny place. From a skylight in the deck-head there hung a brass lamp. I do not quite know what was the function of this lamp for the cabin was lit by electric wall brackets. It was presumably a sort of second string, held in reserve and lit only when the electricity failed. That never happened while I was on board so I never saw the lamp performing any but a purely ornamental function. But what an ornament it was! The Sergeant polished it himself so that its bulbous sides gleamed, throwing back bright points and constellations of light. It caught the eye directly you came into the saloon, swaying gently under the skylight, held in place by three stays so that it could not swing too violently. Round its curved and slender waist the Sergeant had tied a piece of pale blue ribbon in a handsome and feminine bow. Pale blue bows also decorated the electric bracket lamps. On one bulkhead of the cabin was a mirror with a shelf beneath it, edged by a thin brass rail. You could see yourself eating in the mirror, always a humiliating experience, but the brass rail was polished to a celestial brightness and it, too, was decorated with pale blue bows. I wondered what curious twist there was in the make-up of Sergeant Mace that made him express himself in feminine blue bows. But these were not his only vehicle of expression. His chief pride were the small conical sconces which were stuck on to the mahogany bulkheads by means of rubber adhesive pads like the suckers on the tentacles of a cuttle fish. In these sconces, little horns of plenty, there bloomed eternally red poppies from the waving corn, roses from June gardens and daffodils from the sweet fields of spring. The Sergeant had bought them from Woolworth's with his own money and had thus bestowed upon our little world the treasures of spring, summer and autumn in one act of beneficence. What did it matter that they were of paper? They were fadeless and would never know the sad stain and decay which would so soon have overtaken them had they come not from Woolworth's but from Heaven. As it was the only tarnish that dulled their beauty was a faint film of dust. And that could have been easily removed if anyone but the Sergeant had dared to touch them.

"Real bit o' nature, that is," Jim would say reflectively. "Puts me in mind of my little bit o' garden, like. 'Course, it's only a bit of a yard, like, but I usually grow a bit of something when I'm at home, see. Just to give the place a touch of brightness, as the saying is."

One of these little offerings was stuck to the bulkhead above the side of the table along which we had to edge our way to our places. Sparks, whose feet seemed to be a continual embarrassment to him, could never get either in or out without knocking it down.

"Like a bleedin' elephant, you are," said the Sergeant one day in exasperation. "What the 'ell's the use of me tryin' to make the place proper for a great bastard like you?"

Another of the Sergeant's fancies was to decorate the bulkheads, the little flower vases themselves and the lamp brackets with the labels from tins that contained a particular brand of fruit. These depicted a lady in a high white wig and a huge feathered Gainsborough hat. She pleased the Sergeant's taste. Miniatures of Her Grace the Duchess of Devonshire, or whoever it was, gazed haughtily down at us from a dozen eminences as we ate. As the trip went on and the tins became used up the Duchess increased and multiplied around us until it was hard to know where any more of these lovely ladies could be accommodated.

But on the deckies' mess-room across the alleyway no hand had lavished any attention at all. Nothing relieved the austerity of the bare wooden bulkheads except a large printed notice which explained that in gutting fish all the blood must be washed out of the body cavity and that, since all on board were sharers, it was in the interest of all to see that the gutting and washing were carefully and thoroughly carried out. Under this stern admonition, this perpetual reminder of their livelihood, the humbler members of our little company ate, laughing, swearing and jostling one another over their food.

I shared the chaste exclusiveness of the saloon with Skipper, Jim, Sparks and the Chief Engineer.

The Skipper, on the occasions when he came down to meals, took the head of the table. When we were on the grounds and fishing was in full swing he often stayed on the bridge and had a bowl of soup or sandwiches taken up to him by Jack Johnson. But when he came down he made a rather grand entrance. " He ain't matey like some skippers," Jim explained. " Never see him yarning with the lads, like, or stopping to pass the time o' day." Indeed the Skipper made rather a point of this aloofness and sometimes astonished me by referring to the deck-hands as " the slaves " or " the brats." But Jim often stood in the saloon doorway exchanging back-chat with the deckies, and the Bo'sn also, who ate in their mess, would often fill the entrance to the saloon with his enormous bulk, rolling a cigarette and throwing verbal bombs, loaded with expletives, among us. And later, when they got to know me better, I was myself seldom allowed to pass through the deckies' mess without one of them saying:

"Come on, Dick. Come and sit here and talk to us chaps."

But it was some time before the barriers fell down sufficiently for this. You had to pass through the deckies' mess to reach the saloon and I felt their inquiring, slightly suspicious eyes upon me on my way in and on my way out twice a day for a fortnight. Sometimes one of them would come to the saloon door and pause there a second or two to look at me while I ate. Under their direct and questioning gaze I felt like an insect on the stage of a microscope, disembowelled. Sandy, the Second Engineer, submitted me to this rigorous inspection through the door of the saloon regularly every day, pausing sometimes in the alleyway for as much as two or three minutes, chewing a corner of the sweat rag that he wore round his neck and directing upon me a hard and unflinching stare like a searchlight. One day, thinking that something must be done about this, I met his gaze with an equally hard and unflinching stare and then ended it with a sinister and knowing wink. Whereupon he came into the saloon and sat down beside me, still chewing the corner of his sweat rag. He squared his elbows on the fiddle.

"Well," he said. "And what d'ye think to this fishin' now?"

And this, I found, was a kind of password to friendly relations, an ice breaker. It was said a dozen times to me at the beginning of the trip. "Well, what d'ye think to this fishin' now?" It required no answer. It answered itself. " Mug's game, ain't it? "

" Soup? " said the Sergeant.

" Yes, please." And I handed him my plate across the crowded table. A huge metal tureen, almost a tank, of thick lentil soup, like a kind of porridge, stood on the table in the deckies' mess. They helped themselves from it, but we in the saloon were privileged. We had it ladled out to us. So presently the Sergeant brought my plate back and I held it up under my chin with one hand to eat it, as you must in a rolling ship so as not to upset it into your lap.

The food was piled upon the table in magnificent but somewhat grubby abundance. All the dishes and pots were wedged firmly together in the fiddles so that they could not ride about the table and spill their contents. If you moved one of them to help yourself from it you had to wedge it in place again firmly when you had finished. In the middle of the table was an array of dingy bottles. Every conceivable sauce and condiment that was ever made or invented was there, but often in curiously inappropriate vessels. There was a quart beer bottle full of Worcester sauce. There was O.K. sauce in a lime-juice bottle. There was vinegar in a bottle which had evidently, very long ago, held Burgundy from France. There were pickles in jam jars. And there was an explosive mixture called " North Sea sauce " without which, I was assured, no North Sea skipper would dream of putting to sea. It was part of the necessary equipment of every trawler and every drifter that ever sailed. It was made of vinegar and mustard and went with anything. It had the sublime virtue of all sauces, the property of making everything taste exactly the same and of drowning all flavour whatsoever. But none of these bottles and jars that clinked together in the middle of the table bore any label to explain their contents. You had to pick them up and smell them to find out what they held. You knew soon enough then. Their contents congealed in unsavoury incrustations around their mouths and ran in streaks down their necks like gummy tears. Large metal canisters poured out a rain of salt or pepper from their domed tops.

In the middle of the table was a huge dish of stew, or a confusion of congealing mutton chops, or slabs of beef or mutton like tombstones. You used your soup plate for the second course, speared the meat with your fork and conveyed it through the air across the table to your plate. You reached out unceremoniously across your neighbour if necessary to do this. But sometimes the Sergeant was there to help you. He displayed astonishing dexterity and could flip a piece of meat across a distance of two or three feet from its dish to your plate with a single swift motion of a fork.

There was a great open dish of potatoes and another containing a mass of cabbage that looked like something dredged up from the bottom of the sea.

"Good for the blood, that is," said the Sergeant smacking a great wet pad of it on to my plate.

Potatoes ran out towards the end of the trip so that

the day came when the Sergeant said, "No more spuds. Spuds is finished. Split peas instead." So in addition to the wet mass of cabbage another, equally wet and equally massive, was slapped down upon our plates.

I was conscious of making a deliberate effort not to eat as though I came from a world where a different, though not necessarily superior, knife and fork technique was the rule.

The method of using a knife and fork and of conveying food from the plate to the mouth is a peculiar and characteristic thing. It belongs to a people as a marriage custom does, or a language or a manner of observing Christmas. It is almost a national thing, very nearly a matter of politics, for every nation defends its own particular method of eating with a vehemence that is almost religious. An American, for instance, will tell you that it is practically a crime against society to use both the knife and the fork at the same time, as we do, and to convey the food to the mouth with the fork while the knife hovers indeterminately above the plate. The proper way to eat, they say, is to cut everything into small pieces first and then lay the knife aside, change the fork from the left to the right hand and then eat with the fork only, keeping it poised delicately in the air, like a bird, between its recurrent dives towards the plate. If the knife has to be used again the fork is changed back to the left hand and the knife taken up with the right, so that eating becomes an exceedingly complicated ceremonial dance performed with the hands above the plate. We, on the other hand, think all this is very elegant and ever so refined but needlessly elaborate. But with what horror, not unmixed with amused contempt, do we regard the continental habit of eating with the wrists on the table and the knife and fork supported on the edge of the plate! And above all, how we recoil from the spectacle of the knife carried up to the mouth! But now I was to learn, and did my best to acquire, a new technique. I had not realized, it seemed, until I came aboard the *Lincoln Star* what a delicate and useful instrument the knife can be. It can, I soon perceived, be put to all kinds of uses other than those of merely cutting and spreading which had never before occurred to me. It could, of course, be used, and always was used, instead of a spoon. It was introduced into the mouth with a carelessness and abandon that I never succeeded in acquiring for fear of cutting my lips. Sandy, when he ate in the saloon as he occasionally did, used to bring his face right down to the plate and shovel his food into his mouth from the opposite side of the plate with the knife and fork alternately. Then again you could use your knife as a spear, as the Chief Engineer used his, to spear potatoes, pieces of bread or cheese, holding it short, half-way along the blade. And, again, it could be used to emphasize an argument or drive home a point, as Jim always used it, waving it blade foremost over the table in the face of whomever he was addressing. "It's like this here, see," he would say, his elbow on the table and his knife wagging emphatically above the array of bottles. "Now don't be coming that with me, see, because this is something I do know." Or your knife, if you knew how, could be whipped out from your belt, flourished superbly in the air and snapped down upon an imaginary rifle as the Sergeant, in moments of military fervour and abandon, was accustomed to use it on Saturday evenings at tea time when you said, choking between mouthfuls, "That's a grand drop of cake, old soldier!"

On Saturday at dinner time a ceremony took place which, like the Sergeant's cake, marked off the sixth day and made it a day above the others in the week. This was the draw for the football sweep. The chief value of this function was, indeed, perhaps just this, that it marked down one day in the week as just a little different from other days. It was a milestone and each draw marked out the trip into yet another weekly length. You could say, "Next time we have a sweep we shall be on our way home." Or "Sweep after next we'll soon be seeing old Grimsby again." And it brought into lives, whose sameness and lack of interest dulled the senses, just a slight keen scent of something from outside, something new and different. It was as though each week the Goddess of Fortune passed by our little world and swept it with the hem of her garment. Eagerly we reached out and touched it. Eagerly they touch it in British ships on Saturday on all the seven seas when those magic, eye-brightening names come over the air from home—Liverpool United, Sheffield Wednesday, Charlton Athletic, Aston Villa and the rest.

On the first Saturday of the trip Sparks, who ran the sweep, said to me a little doubtfully:

"Don't know whether you'd care to join our football sweep. Always have one, you know, every Saturday."

"Of course," I said.

I am one of those people who never win a sweep. The Goddess of Fortune never brushes me with the hem of her garment and it does, indeed, seem as though my Guardian Angel frowns and puts up his sword whenever I try my luck. But no, I am mistaken. I remember I did once win a sweep, once only. There were thirty of us, all students, coming back from some excursion or other in Devon. I recall that it was all very jolly, with rather spotty young men in grey flannels and nondescript Amazonian young women in blazers. We sang, "John Brown's Body" and "Sing Polly-wolly-doodle All the Day," a refrain, I have always thought, which reaches the summit of fatuity. We got bored with that presently because nobody knew any more songs that we could sing in mixed company so we organised a threepenny sweepstake on the exact time, to within a minute, of our arrival back in the main square of Plymouth. To my astonishment I won it and carried away from the charabanc, through the streets of the town, a hat containing ninety pennies. But that is only one out of hundreds of sweepstakes in which I have since become somewhat grudgingly involved. I have guessed the weight of cakes and of babies. I have allowed myself to be ensnared by promises of trips to Clacton, free visits to unsuccessful plays, Christmas turkeys. I have imagined myself the proud and grateful recipient of fat cheques, double-entrance saloons and labour-saving houses at Gidea Park.

But all in vain. None of these luxuries and delights is evidently to be thus easily acquired by me.

It is the same with games of chance at which I always lose. In any case I am not a born gambler. I feel slightly guilty if I win and wonder vaguely whether I ought not to give the money to charity, but never get farther than wondering. And I am simply infuriated if I lose and am convinced secretly that somebody has cheated. So I never play cards or games of chance if I can help it because they arouse in me these un-Christian and unnatural emotions. As for card games that require skill, I leave them to those who have that strange and occult gift, the card sense, which is in me utterly lacking along with other occult gifts, such as clairvoyance, water divining, thought reading and the power to foretell the future.

So when I said, "Of course I will," I felt quite safe. I knew I should not win any of their hard-earned money by the underhand method of choosing the right piece of paper from a box.

The sweepstake was run on the simplest lines. The name of each football team in the first division of the League was written by Sparks on a separate slip of paper which was folded and placed in a box. In another box were similar folded slips bearing the names of all those participating in the sweepstake. Sparks and two other persons took part in the draw. One called out the name of each man in turn, drawing the slips with the names at random from the box. After every name the second person taking part in the draw selected two slips of folded paper at random from his box and called out the names of the two football teams written on them. Thus for every man's name Sparks wrote down those of two football teams. This was done at dinner-time and there was breathless suspense until the radio news bulletin at six-thirty in the evening. The lucky man whose teams had between them scored the highest number of goals was the winner of a prize of about sixteen shillings, since the entrance fee for the sweep was a shilling and every member of the crew took part in it.

It was my high honour and privilege to take part in the draw on each of the four Saturdays I was on board. I had the box with the names of the teams in it and Jack Johnson had the box containing the names of the crew. Sparks sat with his pencil point poised over his list and wrote down what we called out to him with his elbows squared and a black forelock drooping over the paper. Jack Johnson performed his part of the ceremony with a priestly air, rather suspicious of me and of my competence at first, doubtful whether I was capable of carrying out my side of the job and on the look-out for blunders, which, of course, I made, giving him the opportunity to direct at me his dark and glittering looks full of ancient contempt.

"Skipper!"

A moment while I fumble, with fingers that seem unaccountably like bananas, in the box for two pieces of paper.

"Huddersfield—Liverpool United."

"Mate!"

"Bolton Wanderers—Chelsea."

The others stand around watching, bending eagerly forward, their hands on the table or their arms around each other's shoulders. In their eyes is a light which does not often shine at other times, the light of eager interest. As I call out the teams after each of their names they explode into various comment.

"Coo! Christ! Ain't you in luck an' all?"

"Ah, just the sort o' couple o' bleedin' useless teams I would get."

"Chief Engineer."

"Sheffield Wednesday and—and," I hesitate a moment. "P.N.E. What's P.N.E.?" I ask doubtfully, and am at once conscious of the futility and ignorance of the question.

"Why! Preston North End, of course!" they say, incredulous at my lack of elementary general knowledge.

So presently Jack Johnson calls out the last name from the only remaining slip of paper in his box. But, horror! I, too, have only one slip left in my box. I ought to have two, two teams for every name. I have made the crowning blunder of a misdraw and, under the steady gleam of Jack Johnson's dark eye, I am confounded and put to shame. However, no wrath descends upon my head such as has descended in politer and more exalted circles under similar circumstances. For in my time I have often misdealt at cards and revoked at bridge and trumped my partner's ace with terrifying and never-to-be-forgotten results. "Well, I mean to say, I *ask* you——" But in this company I felt that to misdraw was something that anyone might do and that my doing it was not due to the fact that I had possibly been dropped from a great height when very young, or was in need of a drastic surgical operation on the brain, or had most unfortunately been educated at one of the lesser public schools. They laughed and put it right somehow and when I offered to draw over again Sparks said "Bloody 'ell, no! What does it matter anyway?" and threw back his drooping forelock with a jerk of his head.

Every Saturday evening there was an excitement and expectancy in our community such as no international crisis could possibly arouse. Hitler might shout and rave or Mussolini boast. The massed thunder of "Sieg heil!" and the mounting crescendo of "Duce! Duce! Duce!" might reverberate from the receiving set in Sparks' little den, sending shivers of foreboding down my spine, but for the others these were nothing in their effect to the stimulus provided by the grave and cultured voice of the B.B.C. intoning, "Bolton Wanderers—one, Charlton Athletic—nought. Sheffield Wednesday—two, Liverpool United—one."

On the last Saturday of the trip Sparks said to me triumphantly:

"Well, you're in luck to-day."

"Why?" I said absently.

"You've won."

"What?"

"You've won the sweep."

And I cursed the Goddess of Fortune for the hag and beldame that she is.

The Chief Engineer always came into the saloon a

little late for meals wearing a roguish, knowing expression. Some pearl, we felt, was about to be cast before us, some incomparable jest was forming itself upon his lips. But whatever gem of wit or pearl of wisdom it was that was so obviously maturing, it never seemed to come to anything, for he would sit down at the table without saying anything at all and then, spearing a piece of meat, would square his elbows over his plate and begin a disquisition upon his favourite subject, the anatomy of death.

He seemed to be on astonishingly intimate terms, for so young a man, with the grim janitor of this earthly prison. To hear him talk you would think he had himself faced death a hundred times, looked him in the eyes and learnt all his dreadful idiosyncrasies. He knew the signs of approaching death as though he had often heard that footfall on the threshold. He knew how death sounds and looks as though he had sat with him through long hours of night or wrestled with him until the dawn. Or so it seemed. But it is a common enough thing, this morbid study of death, this detailed knowledge of his natural history and anatomy, particularly among the humble and less fortunate. For while death levels he also lifts and exalts at the same time. He lowers the proud but raises and dignifies the lowly. Or so the lowly tell themselves. The rôle we play on the dingy stage of life may be unimportant enough or short enough but it is nearly always allowed to us to make a more or less dramatic exit, holding the stage a little while alone. However small the audience, our going may be dreadful or pathetic, a martyrdom, a vengeance from on high, a release from affliction, a tragedy, a comedy, a blessed falling upon sleep, all according to the affections, prejudices or passions of the onlookers. But, whatever the audience makes of it, the spotlight is on us and us alone, even if only for a few seconds. It was this aspect of death, I think, which had impressed itself on the mind of the Chief Engineer, for in actual fact his apparently intimate knowledge of the dread messenger was based on one brief meeting only. The occasion was the death of a poor, lonely old lady in Gateshead after a long illness throughout which she had been cared for, somewhat sporadically one gathered, by an unmarried daughter. But in some way the old lady's death had so worked upon the imagination of her son that it was now like a theme of macabre music running in his mind.

He was an oldish-looking young man and had a strange greyness about him. Whether this was due to his pale eyes, or to his complexion, or to his untidy tow-coloured hair, or to the fact that he always wore a grey collarless shirt with a sweat-cloth round his neck, I cannot say. But, coming into the saloon as though he were about to fire off some unguessed and unrivalled drollery, he would sit down at the table, this promise unfulfilled, and begin talking into his plate.

"Just like going to sleep, it was. I got a telephone message about eleven o'clock from my elder sister, the unmarried one, that is, what had nursed her all through. 'Come over, Tom,' she says. 'She's sinking fast.' So, of course, I went over there quick as I could and Sis met me at the door. 'She's asking for you,' she says. So I went up and there she was lying quiet and peaceful and when I came into the room she looked at me, though I don't think she really saw me. Must have heard me, I reckon. 'That you, Tom?' she says. 'Yes, Ma,' I says. 'It's me.' 'Good boy, Tommie,' she says. 'Good boy!' And she patted my hand and never moved again. . . ."

This vivid depiction of that little scene, a brave old woman meeting death calmly, always embarrassed me a little for it seemed to force me to look at something I ought not to see, something not intended for my eyes. It was like peeping through a bedroom keyhole. But the Chief seemed glad to have a new ear to pour the story into. And pour it he did many times before the trip was done.

But in the evening after tea, when the Sergeant had cleared away the confusion of dishes, and removed the sauce bottles, he took the cloth and the fiddles off the table and spread over it a stained square of faded damask with a fringe. In the centre, if the rocketing movement of the saloon were not too violent, he placed a vase of those fadeless blooms that he rejoiced in. After that he slapped down upon the table a pack of thumbed and greasy playing cards. "Ah, nice game o' solo!" It was then that a gleam came into the rather dull eyes of the Chief Engineer. The face of death began to fade and its awful outlines to become blurred. The bright features of the Goddess of Fortune took their place.

For the Chief was an expert at cards, one of these astonishing creatures in whose nimble fingers cards behave as though they had a life of their own. He was ready to play at any hour of the day or night and handled the pack with a dexterity and expertness of born long practice. And I never saw him playing without a pile of money before him larger than that in front of anyone else at the table. Unlike me he basked in the favour of the Goddess of Fortune. Or else he was just good at cards. In either case he was equally unlike me.

One day the Sergeant said to me, " Like a game? Make you a nice cup o' tea, too, if you like. What about a nice game o' solo? " I felt I could not very well decline this friendly invitation so, fearing the worst but hoping for the best, I went aft into the saloon and sat down at the damask cloth with the Chief Engineer and the Bo'sn and Jim.

I think I have in my time played every card game known. And yet, whenever I take up a pack of cards, I do so afresh. I begin as a novice every time with my mind a virgin blank and have to learn all over again. I began at the beginning again that evening and learnt with tribulation, not to say humiliation, under the dull eye of the Chief Engineer, and a bombardment of expletives from the Bo'sn, the game of solo whist. And now, I regret to say, I am as ignorant again as I was before, my mind swept clean and emptied of everything they so industriously pumped into it. I could no more explain here in black and white how you play the game than I could explain the integral calculus which I learnt with so much blood and tears twenty years ago. Alas! Perhaps in this respect, this lack of retentiveness or of concentration, I am a throw-back to some simian ancestor and part of my personality is still, metaphorically, hanging upside down by the tail and throwing nuts among the branches!

A veil over that most embarrassing contest of wits! I had not change available and paid in slips of paper bearing the letters I.O.U. for various amounts. The largest pile of these at the end of the game was heaped in front of the Chief Engineer. But it was not these that worried me. In my sleep still I hear the Bo'sn shouting:

" That's bloody bad play, that is! What the bleedin' 'ell d'you want to go an' play that for? You knew I had the ace. Christ Almighty! You'll never win that way, my lad! "

And the Chief Engineer turned his pale eyes upon me and slowly shook his head.

" Never mind," said the Sergeant. " Make yer a nice cup o' tea."

And when the Chief, finally laying aside the cards, took up his favourite theme once more, at least one member of his audience was all ears to hear how the old lady in Gateshead died.

CHAPTER VII

Beneath the forward well-deck was the fish-room where the fish were to be stored on shelves in ice. It reached forward from the stokehold bulkhead under the bridge housing to the fo'c'sle bulkhead and thus occupied almost the entire fore part of the ship. The fish-room was traversed by the pipes of a refrigerating plant and was divided into four compartments communicating with each other by a central alleyway. Each compartment had a square hatch in the deck above.

In Grimsby, before we sailed, the foremost compartment of the fish-room had been filled with ice which would be used when the fish were stored later on upon the shelves in the other three compartments. In Blyth the after compartment was filled with coal for the passage north.

When we coaled in Blyth all the ship's hatches were battened down, all port-holes screwed up and all doors shut. Coal-dust enveloped the *Lincoln Star* in a black cloud and settled as a jet glistening rain. The coal came thundering into the after compartment of the fish-room from the coaling derrick through a great funnel that hung its snout, like the vomiting proboscis of a huge beast, down the after hatchway. As the black torrent roared down dust seaped like a vapour from every crevice and joint in the proboscis, floating away upon the grey air of Blyth. Stocky grimy Geordies hopped about, shovelling, spitting, swearing and shouting to each other above the din of the avalanche.

Tiny stood on the jetty watching them. When they had finished he set to work with a hose and cleaned up the mess they had left behind, blaspheming and laughing all the time. He was known as Tiny because he was a giant, nearly seven feet tall and broad in proportion, with a jovial red face that beamed incessantly, displaying a magnificent disarray of yellow teeth. Some years ago Tiny had lost an arm in a dockside accident so that he could no longer work as a coalie and all his giant strength was of no use to him. Instead he turned honest pennies by making himself useful to ships. He ran errands for the men, striding away roaring up to the shops to buy for them last-minute packets of fags, tobacco, a cap, newspapers, or perhaps a bottle of beer. The honesty and dispatch with which he performed these small services had made him known and trusted by the hundreds of trawlermen that came in and out of Blyth. "Get Tiny to do it," they said. Tiny very often got the price of a drink for these errands. He never spent it but was immediately off on another errand, thus making the price of two drinks. It all helped, especially when one was on the dole. Besides these services he would, for a shilling or two, watch the ship if the crew wanted to go ashore for the evening and, for another shilling or so, performed the useful office of caller-out. He would go the round of all the places where trawlermen might possibly be found so as to get the crew together before the ship sailed. For he knew them all—all the bars and the dives and the joints

—and knew all the arts of coaxing men out of them, out of bars and out of beds, cajoling some, booting others, carrying others feet foremost. When, after weeks or months or years, they came back to Blyth again Tiny would remind them all of past epics. "Remember last time you was 'ere, Bill? Heaviest bastard I ever had to carry out of a pub in my life!" They all knew Tiny. "Come and fetch us at eleven, Tiny," they would say. And at eleven sharp Tiny would be there, filling the doorway of the bar, peering through the haze of smoke and saying, "Any o' them bastards from the *Lincoln Star* here? Come on, lads. Time to get going." And they went.

When the coaling was over Tiny washed down with a hose and made the deck shipshape again, performing miracles of dexterity with his poor shortened arm. When the *Lincoln Star* sailed he stood on the jetty and waved her bon-voyage with this stump, a gigantic smiling figure, before he turned to yet another ship and did for her and for her men the same small invaluable services.

The coal in the after compartment of the fish-room was additional to that in the bunkers and was used up first on the passage north. For this purpose it had to be shovelled through a tunnel which led through the bulkhead into the stokehold.

Billie and Sambo, the trimmers, did this for a spell during every watch on passage north. Day and night at intervals you could hear the scrape and rasp of their shovels down there, the rattle of the coal as they shot it down the tunnel, and their voices laughing or singing while they worked.

Billie came from the south of Ireland though nearly all his life, since he could remember, he had lived in Grimsby. Or rather he had lived mostly at sea and came back every now and then to his mother's house in Grimsby. He was not yet eighteen and was wiry and supple as a young tree. His sinewy body, black as a negro's, glistening with sweat and clad only in a torn singlet and dungaree trousers, moved rhythmically over the shovel back and forth, keeping low like a man with a scythe, swinging round with a scrape and a single lunge outwards as the coal shot from his shovel in a black mass down the tunnel. Coal-dust rolled up from the place where he flung it as he swung back for more, bent and lunged again. Back and forth Billie swung, keeping low and smiling. He smiled all the time as he worked. Presently he stood up, wiping the black sweat from his forehead with a cloth or with the back of his hand.

"Like a go?" he said. He laughed and blew a drop of sweat outwards in an arc from the tip of his nose.

"Don't think I'd be much good at that job," I said.

"Go on! It's easy. Keep your shovel low and take your coal from underneath. Chuck it well out and down the tunnel. The farther you chuck it the less dust you get."

So I took off my coat and jersey and went at it. I might have done all right if I had been as wiry as Billie and had shovelled coal watch and watch for years as he had. But, since I had never shovelled coal before, except on rare occasions, and since, moreover, I had passed the eighteenth milestone somewhere about the time when Bille was born, I found that the shovel-loads of coal I sent down the tunnel were not half the size of his and seemed to go not half the distance. I made the dust rise about us like a dust-storm without making any very great impression on the black cliff before me. And in no time the sweat was pouring off my forehead and there was a tightness under my midriff. Billie watched me, leaning one hand upon the bulkhead.

"Ah!" he said, laughing as I straightened up after a few minutes. "You want a bit of practice, that's all!"

Billie had a natural grace and the charm of manner that belongs to the southern Irish, a certain elegance of speech and gesture that they share with Latins and which, I have often thought, makes us English look like louts beside them. Indeed I could not help feeling that Billie would have been just as self-possessed and at ease if the black walls of the tunnel had then and there faded away and become the walls of a London drawing-room, with him in his blackened singlet and dungarees in the middle of it. He would have dealt perfectly with the situation. "Well, this is a fine state for me to be in, to be sure." He knew how to say the things that please, such as "All you want's a bit of practice. Pick it up in no time, you would," after I had given a short display of inadequacy at shovelling coal in his tunnel. Or he would say, "What about you coming down to the tunnel? I could do with a bit of pleasant company down there." People have given gold and treasure and spent themselves in vain just to have those little, perhaps meaningless, but important things said to them.

Billie's ambition was to come to London. When off duty he would come up on to the bridge and lean upon the rail of the narrow bridge-deck, plying me with questions about that enchanted city. "You're a lucky chap to live in London. That must be a grand place, that must. The lights an' all. What are the tarts like there? Tell you what, I'm saving up to buy a motor-bike so I can come up to London and see the Cup Final. Then you can show me round when I come. What about it? Will you?"

"Why, of course I will."

But he won't come. Three days in port and Billie rejoins his ship with nothing put by towards that motor-bike, the magic internal combustion carpet that is to take him to the city of dreams. Luckily for him, perhaps, London will always remain the fairy city with the jewelled spires and streets of lapis-lazuli and gold, dim, remote and legendary. The less dazzling but nearer and more accessible attractions of Grimsby will keep it so for ever!

Billie's opposite number, Sambo, worked in the tunnel during Billie's watch below. You could tell whether it was Billie or Sambo whose shovel you could hear scraping rhythmically down in the stokehold because Sambo always sang while he worked. He sang those sentimental songs that find so much favour in the stokeholds of ships. He had a good clear tenor voice but gave to it a curious whining intonation which was intended to add pathos. He sang on the lunge outwards when he shot his shovel-load of coal down the tunnel and on the swing back, interrupted his melody a moment when his great arms thrust at the foot of the black cliff and sang on again with the next lunge. He had none of Billie's graces and, with his blackened face and eyes ringed with soot, he looked the toughest man in the world. A greasy lock of hair curled over the peak of his grimy cap. He was always gently puzzled about something, perhaps indeed about life in general. That would not be surprising. Frequently he lifted his cap between the forefinger and thumb of one hand to scratch his head with a third finger with an air of deep perplexity. But, on the whole, life seemed to be a genial and amusing mystery to him and, on receiving the really quite simple explanation of some conundrum set him by life, he would walk away laughing and shaking his head, or scratching the top of it with his third finger. "Well, that's a rum 'un, that is an' all."

But when we reached the "banks" after four days' steaming Billie and Sambo gave up their subterranean occupations and came up on deck. They worked among the other deck-hands for as long as fishing continued, handling the trawl, gutting, washing and stowing the fish. They changed their black singlets and dungaree trousers for thick jerseys, fear-nought leggings and high rubber thigh-boots. Billie washed the coal-dust from his face and out of his hair but still the signs of his former occupation remained as heavy black encircling rings like a theatrical make-up. Sambo, however, kept his mask of grime longer than Billie and bleached slowly in the unaccustomed light of day.

Besides Billie and Sambo there were four deck-hands whose sole business was that of paying out and heaving in the trawl, rigging and repairing the gear, washing, gutting and stowing the fish. They did these things under the supervision of the Mate and the Bo'sn.

The deckie is a humble person, the humblest but perhaps, after all, the most necessary in that little community. He works many hours a day and night in every conceivable kind of weather, cursing when the weather is foul, laughing when it is fair, for weeks on end for two pounds five a week and a share of twopence in the pound on the takings of the trip. In the winter the decks and rails, rigging and stanchions are caked with ice. On dirty nights the fore-deck is knee-deep or even, when she rolls badly, waist-deep in icy water. The men work with torn and bleeding fingers. They slip and stumble and lurch about the deck, break arms and legs, trip over flicking wires, or rupture themselves. Sometimes they are carried overboard into the heaving icy darkness. They curse and laugh and spit. They get little sleep on the "banks" for the trawling never stops for a fortnight or three weeks, if the fishing is good, from the first haul, when they arrive on the grounds, to the day when the Skipper decides that there is no more room to stow the fish or that the time has come to turn homewards. During those days the deckies sleep only in short spells. They must always be ready to go on deck instantly if the trawl should hitch or tear or the gear part on some obstruction. Each haul lasts two or three hours. Directly the trawl

Deckie.

comes up it is emptied of its catch and sent over the side again. While it is fishing the catch is sorted, gutted, washed and stowed below. The deck is washed down. If the fishing is good the catch is stowed and the deck washed down only just in time to bring in the trawl and set to work again. Then the deckie gets no sleep at all for days. In any case eighteen hours continuous work a day is not unusual. But it only makes the deckie curse a bit more and drink more over-sweetened tea.

The deckie has no special knowledge of seamanship beyond what he picks up during the course of years at the game. But he can acquire a mate's ticket and then a skipper's ticket by sitting for a Board of Trade exam, a dread ordeal to which most of them submit sooner or later. Some pass and some fail. Those who pass cannot always get jobs as mates or skippers in these days, though the best of them usually do so. Both the Skipper of the *Lincoln Star* and Jim, the mate, began as deckies and worked their way through the exams and through the hard schools of North Sea and deep-water experience. But, with or without a skipper's or a mate's ticket, the deckie has these other invaluable qualifications, patience, humour, kindliness. They take him through many arduous exams not set by the Board of Trade. He acquires them, as they can only be acquired, by living constantly at close quarters with his shipmates, sharing every thought and action, enduring common hardships and common dangers. But you acquire other things that way. You grow a shell.

The four deckies, with Billie and Sambo and two

firemen, lived in a little fuggy holy-of-holies, the deckies' fo'c'sle, right for'ard in the bows. A narrow companion way led down to it and, through the fo'c'sle head, a tall thin chimney carried away the acrid fumes of the coal stove that warmed this tiny burrow. A trail of smoke and sparks continually fled away from it upon the wind. No one, who did not himself live there, ever went down to the fo'c'sle, except the Bo'sn, and very occasionally the mate. It was, as it always is, the most private part of the ship and its privacy was a precious thing, closely guarded. It is always so in ships. For the fo'c'sle is the home of the men who live in it, their own special place, their private house, their castle. All that each man had to call his own, in the *Lincoln Star*, was his narrow fo'c'sle bunk. It was the only place where he could shut himself off for a time from his constant close companions or where he could think his own thoughts to himself. A small locker was all the room he had in which to keep his Lares and Penates, little possessions whose value is not of this world, the letters someone wrote, the snapshots of someone, the brooch that someone wore. Here were laid away the shore-going suit, carefully folded and awaiting its thirty-six-hour spell of duty that came once in three or four weeks, the shoes, the clean shirt. These and a book or two and some old magazines, perhaps, were the things that linked them to the other life ashore, slender links but strong.

I saw little of the deckies, except on deck, or when one of them took over the wheel, or in their mess during that half-hour of relaxation after tea or dinner.

These latter occasions were only towards the end of the trip. For over a fortnight they eyed me in silence as I passed through their mess on the way to the saloon. But one by one they introduced themselves in the wheel-house.

"Well—what do ye think to this fishin' now?"

One day Sambo said, "What's yer name? What do we call you?"

I told him. Next time I went through the deckies' mess to tea a voice said, "Evenin', Dick."

Next day they said, "Come and talk to us chaps."

That meant sitting at their table listening to their abuse of each other, to the endless unfolding of their adventures ashore, sexual and alcoholic; to their views about football and boxing; to their discussions about the chances of winning that long hoped-for fortune on some horse or other. But I found I was doing all that was required of me if I only sat there and listened without saying a word.

The four deckies, besides Billie and Sambo who were really trimmers, were Jake and Joe and Harry and Tom. They were known by these names and these only. Indeed I never heard what the outer world called some of them. Perhaps they left their shore-going names behind them when they sailed or perhaps they had lost them through disuse. But they were honest straightforward names and none was longer or grander or higher-sounding than any other. Dick was no more than Tom or Jake. In this little world, at any rate, he was a good deal less though no one ever hinted that there was any difference. Indeed I was astonished to find how unquestioningly my presence was accepted among them when once they had become used to the way I spoke or to the look of my face or whatever it was that was foreign about me and not of their world. I was not asked, except casually, where I lived or what I did or how I justified my existence. Nor, apparently, did they wish to know what I was doing there among them. I began to think that they welcomed me there as a link with that life ashore which they knew went on without them. I meant, perhaps, that the world was not revolving in callous indifference to their existence.

These four, Jake, Joe, Harry and Tom, only slowly developed individual characteristics for me. Only by degrees did they become separate entities. At first they formed a collective unit but slowly individual differences began to break up the united front they presented to my consciousness. I found that when Jake was at the wheel he hummed incessantly, but just audibly, a song that had no ending and no particular refrain. He was a man of few words but when you spoke to him he said, "Yurss," and then considered a long time before committing himself further. Neither Joe nor Harry spoke much either but fell often into that state of abstraction, mentally withdrawn, a kind of Yogi, which men seem able to induce so readily at sea. Their eyes over the wheel, fixed on the flecked horizon rising and falling, seemed to become glazed, their lips half open with a cigarette dangling from them and spilling unregarded ash. It is the hypnotic effect of the sea, the limitless flat face of it, which drains the mind of thought. Joe, in this abstracted state, looked like a lizard which remains fixed, motionless for hours upon a stone. He had a brown sharp face and little beady eyes, alert but stony, unwinking beneath the peak of his cap.

But Tom was fond of company and talked a lot in the wheel-house. He had a strained husky voice, made so, he reckoned, by too much beer and too much smoking. And too much skirt, he supposed. Tom's head was enormously thick between the ears, like the head of an all-in wrestler, and shaven so close that his hair behind the neck was little more than a kind of iridescence. He had a chest like a barrel; short, thick, bowed legs and powerful arms that ended in wrists that looked as though they could snap bars. Whenever Tom was not smoking one of the brown cigarette butts which lived behind his ear he sucked a matchstick between his discoloured teeth. Very few of these, he boasted, were opposite to one another. He supposed he ought to have them out since he suffered a lot from toothache at sea, but he was always too scared to go to a dentist. He could roll his matchstick swiftly from one corner of his mouth to the other without removing it, but when talking he often took it from between his lips and considered it, holding it between his thumb and forefinger. It helped him to think.

All that Tom said, addressing his matchstick, seemed to express a nostalgia that he felt but did not understand. It was the same with all of them on board the *Lincoln Star*. Their constant talk of their short spells ashore, their eager longing for those thirty-six hours between trips, their talk about them as though each brief interval were the end of labour instead of the prelude to more, burnt into my mind the picture of men trapped by life, held fast, unable to escape. Was I wrong in thinking that I sensed an ache for a kind of life not less arduous but more free? I never heard a word of complaint about their cramped quarters, or about their long hours and hard work, or about the dangers that were part of their daily life. But I thought they looked on life as a bitter, destroying, deadening thing. It had to be endured or escaped from but could not be enjoyed. And they had not, as have the similarly afflicted ashore, an easy way of escape through the cinema, the warm friendliness of pubs, or through women. These came in short spells every once in three weeks and into the thirty-six hours all of joy and pleasure and comfort and ecstasy must be compressed. Only then they lived.

" Monotonous, ain't it—this life? " said Tom one day, studying his matchstick reflectively.

" There's a certain sameness about it, I should think," I replied—fatuously, I admit, but the question was its own answer.

" D'you know what I've been doin' all this last watch, Dick? "

" What? "

" Lookin' at a picture of my old woman."

" All the watch? "

" Aye. That's right. Bleedin' hell! " And he blasphemed softly and stuck the matchstick in his mouth again.

Deckie-learner.

CHAPTER VIII

About half the earth's surface lies more than two miles beneath the sea. That is ninety million square miles or two-thirds of the extent of all the oceans. In these abysses lies a cold dark world of utter stillness, far out of reach of the action of waves or of any disturbance from above. The refuse washed from the land by rivers and worn away by waves, dropped far out over the ocean floor, does not reach these still and secret depths. Only a soft impalpable mud accumulates there slowly from the fine rain of dead things that never ceases.

The upper layers of the ocean, especially those within reach of the sunlight, are peopled by dense clouds of minute floating life, microscopic things within skeletons of lime or glass, often of amazing beauty, cunningly and strangely made. Most important among these are the plants of the sea which make a vast pasture of the colder oceans. Teeming microscopic herds graze upon them, and directly or indirectly, they support all the life of the sea, even to the Leviathan snorting round the pole. To the naked eye these plants are only a green slime, sometimes so dense that it thickens and colours the water itself. But the green is the same as the green of trees and flowers, trapping the sunlight as do the summer leaves. In the spring this green plant slime bursts into abundance. In the winter it dies away and the tiny skeletons sink down and settle on the ocean floor.

In this cold, dark, soundless region, out of reach of sunlight, undisturbed by the action of waves, where this gentle rain from heaven finally comes to rest, live nightmare creatures that prey on one another, savage, swift, voracious, but often little and frail as paper. Here are fish with bodies like threads but with huge mouths and sabre teeth. Here are others with comparatively gigantic stomachs like sacks. Some have enormous eyes that entrap the least suspicion of light that filters down to them. And others carry little lamps which themselves give out a feeble glow. But none of them can live at a level higher than its own. If brought up from the chill hades where they live they die for the change of pressure turns them inside out.

But towards the continents the sea floor sweeps upwards, gently in some places, abruptly in others. Towards the surface it becomes more and more thickly peopled by things that burrow into, or crawl upon, or wriggle through the oozy mud. Finally, near the coast, the sea floor forms a broad or narrow shelf where the depth is about a hundred fathoms. Here the outflow of rivers and the ceaseless action of waves spread mud and sand layer upon layer. Indeed the shelf is largely formed thus, by the substance of the continents washed from the land and dropped upon the bed of the ocean. In this rich deposit there live, in fabulous abundance, the worms, the molluscs, the crustaceans, all the countless beasts that swarm upon the bottom of the sea and are the food of fishes. In places this continental shelf is narrow, as it is along the coast of Africa, but elsewhere it broadens out and forms great table lands beneath the sea where vast shoals of food fishes spawn and live, sustained by the crawling, burrowing population of the ocean bed. But in the open ocean, far from the land and over deep water, the sea is comparatively empty of fish because there is no food for them. Only on the shallow shelves that border the coasts live those great multitudes of fish that form a harvest for mankind.

These shelves where the fish spawn and live are known to the fishermen as "banks." The slope, where the "bank" turns to plunge into the depths, is known as the "edge." The greatest and, I suppose, the richest banks in the world reach out from the northern coast of Europe, up to the coast of Norway and down to the coast of Spain. They encompass our islands. They form the floor of the North Sea, the Irish Sea, the Norwegian Sea and the Bay of Biscay. Much of the fish that feed the millions of Europe's mouths live and spawn upon them. Fishing ships from all the nations whose coasts border upon those seas sweep to and fro across these banks incessantly with their nets. Men from Britain, from France, from Germany, from Norway and Denmark and Holland share the hardships and dangers of the same trade. At sea, where there are no frontiers, the same wind toughens all their skins, the same cold and the same fogs envelop them all. Those barriers, armed with thorns, that men erect against each other ashore all disappear. There remains a deep respect and regard for those qualities of kindness and tolerance, toughness and endurance which the sea breeds in men from whatever country they may come. "Them Germans," said Tom one day, thoughtfully sucking his matchstick, "is a pretty decent lot o' bastards, I reckon."

But besides these homely grey seas of ours there are other banks which supply the hungry world with fish. There are huge banks around Newfoundland, world-famous for cod. There are others around Spitzbergen, the White Sea and Bear Island, and those off the coast of Iceland for which the *Lincoln Star* was bound. Off the eastern coast of Asia there are banks fished by the Russians and the Japanese, but in the southern hemisphere there are scarcely any fishing grounds of real importance. In general the richest grounds are in the north and in the colder waters, and the tropics are poor in food fish. And for this there are several reasons. In the colder waters there swarms in greatest profusion that floating plant and animal life which dies and rains down like manna upon the creeping, crawling, burrowing things upon the sea bottom. These creatures also die themselves so that their remains make food for the rest. And further, most of these bottom-haunting animals, which are the food of the great shoals of fish, start life as tiny frail young, drifting at the surface, quite unlike the adults they will finally become. They feed, in these young stages, on the plant slime which, in all the colder waters, bursts into thick abundance in the summer and in the winter dies away again.

Around Iceland the banks stretch out irregularly all round the jagged mountainous coastline, roughly following its indentations, for as much in places as eighty miles. A clockwise current sweeps over the banks round and round the island, for where the Gulf Stream strikes the ridge on which the Shetlands and the Faroes stand part of it turns north-west towards Iceland. The rest flows on through a shallow valley between the Shetlands and the Faroes into the Norwegian Sea. Down the eastern coast of Iceland a current flows southwards from the Arctic to join the warm flood from the Gulf Stream and together the two flow round the island clockwise. A current that pours southwards down the Greenland coast, bearing ice and blocking up all that desolate seaboard every winter, may sometimes bear the pack ice up to the North Cape of Iceland, a high northern steep, the northernmost point of the island, looking towards the North Pole. But to the south and east, bathed by the warm stream from the Atlantic, the pack ice never comes and, because of this offshoot from the Gulf Stream, the climate of Iceland is much more mild and gentle than that of Greenland nearby, whose coasts are washed by the chill stream bearing ice down from the north.

On the fourth day out from Grimsby we passed Langanes, a long thin finger of land at the north-eastern corner of Iceland, and came out upon the banks upon the northern side. It was a calm and lovely evening. The dark silhouette of distant mountains reached out a flat arm against the fiery sky. At the end of it one light winked palely like a gem—Langanes Point. A swell ran up out of the veiled east and split itself upon the cliffs of Langanes. In the gathering dark you could just faintly see the leaping white of the breakers, like tongues licking up towards the cliff-tops. In an old picture of the Deluge, I remembered, the hosts of the despairing doomed reached up thus vainly towards the slopes of Ararat and fell back into the flood. We passed another trawler homeward bound, rocking gently over the long swell, her smoke streaming from her funnel, and we waved her good-bye from the bridge-deck.

"Wouldn't mind bein' aboard that," said Tom at the wheel. "Be back in old Grimsby in four days, she will an' all. Ah, well——"

The men were seated on the fore-deck rigging the trawls. There were two trawls, one on each side. The foot-ropes, steel hawsers threaded with iron and wooden bobbins, lay along the scuppers and the trawls themselves had remained throughout the passage north stowed snugly upon them along the rails. The foot-rope that lay along the port scuppers was threaded with huge spherical iron bobbins, the largest in the centre, diminishing in size towards either end. The foot-rope on the starboard side was threaded also with wooden discs like segments of tree-trunk alternating with the iron globes. A rope rigged with iron bobbins only was for use on a "hard bottom" of stones. For a "soft bottom" of mud or sand wooden rollers only were used. The intermediate type of foot-rope, threaded with alternating iron and wooden bobbins, "White Sea rigged" as they say, was used on a mixed bottom, neither very hard nor very soft. The starboard trawl, with the "White Sea" foot-rope, was an old one and the men

The foot-rope. "White Sea" rigged.

were now busy transferring the port trawl, which was newer and in better condition, to the starboard side. Most skippers prefer to trawl from the starboard side if possible since it is easier to handle the ship with the gear to starboard. "Still, you never can tell," said the Skipper dubiously. "I dunno how this old bitch will behave yet. Can't tell till you start." The deckies were fixing a new "belly," a new underside, to the trawl and they sat in a row upon the fore hatches in the dusk, working by the growing illumination of overhead electric lights. The ship rocked gently, pushing the swell aside with a soft continual sigh which made a background for the murmured conversation of the men. You could hear Billie's laugh above the others and occasional explosions from the Bo'sn. Kittiwake gulls flew softly like large grey moths around the ship, fell astern and fluttered ahead again in the dusk.

As their hands moved swiftly to and fro, holding the wooden spools on which the trawl twine was wound, they seemed indeed to be at peace in that quiet moment as people only are at peace when their hands are busy with a skilful familiar task. With the great net sprawling over the deck about their feet they seemed to be quietly and contentedly at work on a gigantic stocking and the swift movement to and fro of their hands had a tranquillizing effect upon them like knitting. On the hatch covers behind them were balls of trawl twine, white and clean. Jack Johnson stood by, cutting the twine into lengths and winding the lengths on to the wooden spools. When any man's spools were exhausted he turned to Jack Johnson and received from him another spool freshly wound. Jack Johnson performed this simple task with a conspiratorial air and refused to be surprised into a smile when the Bo'sn shouted above the swish of the sea:

"Come on, Basher! Look lively with it. We start fishin' to-morrow night, not to-day fortnight."

Tom sucked his matchstick silently as his rough hands went deftly over, under, through. Pulled tight and moved on to the next. Over, under, through. The folds of new netting grew, sprawling in white folds about their feet. Now and then one of them rose, collected the empty mugs of tea and went aft along the deck, to return presently with the mugs filled. And every man paused in his work from time to time, lifted his mug to his lips and placed it by his side again.

They spoke little but laughed occasionally and lit cigarettes. It grew dark and stars came out over all the evening sea. Far off towards the west the lights of other trawlers already on the northern banks glowed tiny and distant and changed their position relative to one another very slowly, like circling planets, as they went about their patient tireless business. The light of Langanes flashed on our port quarter and slowly fell astern, winking in the gathering night.

Behind my grandfather's house there used to be a building called the workshop. The door was always locked when the old man was not working in it and when he was working there it was forbidden, under pain of the most dreadful penalties, to disturb him.

So the place became a mystery to me and I went about in a perpetual state of wonder as to what exactly went on in that forbidden and secret apartment. Grandfather was an alchemist, perhaps, working among huge retorts and dimly bubbling flasks of coloured liquids wringing gold out of base metal. Or was he a magician practising strange nocturnal rites? The fact that the old man distributed about the house, and to his numerous children, my aunts and uncles, an apparently endless succession of somewhat rickety sham Jacobean cabinets, cupboards, bookshelves and what-nots had no connection for me with anything that might go on in that private room behind the house. Even when he displayed them as his own handiwork I suppose I thought he created them by saying, like God, " Let there be a what-not." And there was a what-not.

Then one day I stole in upon him when, in an unguarded moment, he was working with the door open. And I found myself, delighted and amazed, in a private heaven that the old man had made for himself. It was, indeed, as magical as an alchemist's laboratory, for I understood even then the joy and the peace of mind that he achieved there. A long bench ran under the windows. There were racks where chisels of every degree of fineness stood in ranks like yellow soldiers. There was a vice and a lathe and a whetstone. The lathe and the whetstone revolved when you pedalled. There were sweet smelling strips of uncut wood stacked in a corner, beautiful and satisfying, oak and elm and pine. The old man, puffing a curved pipe, his white head haloed in light, was bending over some long straight strips of wood upon the bench. He was cutting fine parallel grooves along them with a chisel, the handle of which he kept tapping gently with a wooden mallet. The little chips flew sweetly off the wood as the chisel moved forward. After that day I used to go often and play about in the workshop when the old man was working there for the taboo was lifted from that moment. The place was no longer forbidden to me. And it lost its mystery, for though I could never understand or gauge the skill that went into the work yet something of the joy and peace of it was communicated to me and understood. I saw growing there, day after day, a Jacobean cupboard with knobbly turned legs, a book-case with drawers beneath that slid sweetly in and out and, most impressive of all, my grandfather's masterpiece, his magnum opus, a folding fretwork screen of Chinese design. It had three gilt knobs on each of the folding leaves which were the final touches, put on one pale sunny day shortly before Christmas. I thought that screen was the most beautiful thing I had ever seen, and I still do. Whenever I see it now, standing in my aunt's drawing-room, I recall the old man's face as he fashioned those complicated knobs and cut with his fine chisels the lines of those aesthetically outrageous patterns. I recall his strong yet subtle hands stroking the wood with love, and how he would get up from the bench and gaze down at what he had done, blowing a great cloud of smoke around his head. Thus on the seventh day, I always think, did the Creator light a pipe and gaze at his handiwork, finding that it was good. That Chinese screen, which has now survived its creator by about fifteen years, stands for many little hopes and despairs long ago finished with, resolved and ended, little difficulties long ago overcome. It crystallizes and makes immortal sudden ideas, flashes of inspiration in the night, anxieties, fear lest it should not be perfect, final triumph. It stands for the joy of creation and of doing something for somebody else.

Sitting on the deck of the *Lincoln Star*, watching the deckies making their trawl, I thought of the Chinese screen and of the happiness which is achieved by men who work with their hands, as they were working and as my grandfather worked, and have skill in their fingers. While their rough strong hands moved swiftly, holding the wooden spools, there came over their faces the look I had seen my grandfather wear as he worked with his chisels. It was an undisturbed and settled look. Sometimes one of them would stop work, get up and spread out a fold of net to look at it. Then he would light a cigarette and gaze at the new length of net for a while with satisfaction before continuing. Again, the Creator gazing at his handiwork and finding that it was good. The making of a trawl was the only thought in their minds at that particular time, even Grimsby and Blyth were forgotten. This was their own work which their hands were trained to do and which they could do supremely well, better than anyone else, these same movements —swift, certain and true. Over, under, through. Pull tight and on to the next. Over, under, through. It was their craft. It was Peter's craft beside Galilee. Perhaps it brought him the same peace.

The trawl grew slowly and spread white over the deck beneath the electric lights. The belly and back of it, the wide upper part of the bag of the trawl, were of large mesh but about two-thirds of its length from the mouth it narrowed down and was made of stouter rope with a very much finer mesh. This was the "cod-end," where the fish would be retained, and it tapered like a finger to where a slip-rope closed an opening at its apex. Underneath the cod-end was a flap of stout strong netting, the "false belly," which would protect the trawl from chafing upon the bottom.

Next morning, in the light of a clear blue day, they finished the trawl. They bound strips of cow-hide on to the outside of the cod-end as a still further protection against chafing. The mouth of the trawl was finished round its rim with stout rope. This was secured to the steel foot-rope with short lengths of chain at intervals between the bobbins. To the head-rope, strung with its spherical glass floats, the mouth of the trawl was secured by lashings.

When it was finished they got up one by one from the hatch covers, lit cigarettes and sat for a long time in the pale northern sunshine, gazing at what they had done.

"Ought to do all right now."

"Be all right so long as we don't tear nowt."

"Tore the belly out of a brand new trawl last trip, first bloody haul. Just here off the North Cape it was an' all."

"Must have 'ad a bleedin' Jonah aboard."

"Don't believe in that stuff, meself."

Over, under, through.

"No more didn't I, till that time I was in the *Northern Flower*. It was like this 'ere, see. . . ."

So, when their hands stopped, it was as though the lid of Pandora's box were lifted once again.

CHAPTER IX

" CALL out, Skipper? "

" Aye, call out, Jake."

Jake left the wheel and went for'ard to call out the hands, disappearing down the narrow companion way which led down to the fo'c'sle. We had arrived upon our fishing grounds.

It was a lovely clear and sunny day. Out of the shining water the jagged outline of the North Cape stood hard against the blue sky. A few plumes of cloud rested upon its shoulders. The almost vanished snows of winter gleamed where they caught the sun upon its topmost heights. In all directions were other ships like ours, a silent preoccupied company, turning and moving slowly with their spankers set. Against the heavens they trailed long bars of smoke that lingered as dark dispersing wreaths or bent themselves into evanescent loops above the summer sea.

The fore-deck had been made ready for work that morning. The battens had been removed from the fish-room hatches. On each side of the hatches the open deck space had been partitioned off into square pens by lengths of board about a foot high. These were the gutting and washing pounds. When the trawl came in the fish would be emptied out into them so that, enclosed by these wooden walls, they would not slide and slither about the deck as the ship rolled. The hoses were ready for washing. The steam was on the winches. The starboard trawl was unlashed ready for shooting. When they had seen that everything was ready the men went below for an hour's sleep. It might be the last they would get, if the fishing was good, for many hours.

When Jake called them out they came running up the companion and on to the deck joking and laughing. The sailor and the fisherman always laugh when the weather is fine, for foul weather is never long remembered. And not only was it fair weather, calm and blue, but to-day the money would begin coming in again. Life moved on a step to-day towards whatever goal or consummation it was moving for each of them. Or rather towards whatever goal they thought it was moving. This day would add something towards Billie's motor-bike, one step nearer to the city of his dreams. At least, it would be Billie's fault if it didn't. It would make up for evenings in Blyth and Grimsby and would straighten matters out a bit. On passage north it had been a shocking, overwhelming thing to notice how flat your wallet was since leaving port. But to-day it would begin to resume its normal shape and to fill out a little, in the imagination anyhow, as trawl after trawl came in. Those thoughts and plans for the future which you had been turning over in your mind last trip began to take shape again after a week or so of melancholy eclipse. They were neither very ambitious nor very important for the most part. There was Billie's motor-bike. There was Tom's resolve to pluck up enough courage to go to a dentist about his teeth. There was Sambo's ambition to have a new blue suit. And there was the Sergeant's new old woman. All these came to light again out of their hiding places on this summer morning when we started fishing. During the succeeding fortnight they enlarged and grew into lusty giants. By the end of the trip they darkened their respective skies. If the fishing was good this trip Billie would buy, not a motor-bike, but a car and miss the next trip so as to come up to London and stay for a fortnight in a posh hotel. Somewhere really smart where they wait on you and clean your shoes and bring you tea in the morning. The King's Cross Hotel, he thought. Would I come to tea with him when he was staying at the King's Cross Hotel? Tom thought he would have all his teeth out and get a complete set of fine new false ones. " Wouldn't know me then, would you, Dick?" He thrust his cap forward on his shaven pate and swaggered up and down the fore-deck with his chest thrown out and arms bent, grinning to display his imaginary dentures where his crooked stumps now were. Sambo had added several shirts to his new blue suit. And as for the Sergeant, he sprang to attention, saluted and presented the new Mrs. Mace, who was, of course, a perfect little peach with fluffy hair and blue eyes. She adored the Sergeant and thought him the bravest and most brilliant man on earth, but unfortunately she existed, as yet, only in her husband's imagination. Jack Johnson alone, perhaps, was wise. He said nothing and made no plans. He knew he would have to hand over all his money, when he got home, to his old man who was black as the ace of spades.

The echo sounding machine on the bridge, with its

flickering dot of light, indicated 92 fathoms. "Well," said the Skipper, peering at it, "I think we'll shoot here and see what luck we get. Sparks, see if you can get the *Knight of Castile* and ask him what luck he's had."

"Aye, Skip," said Sparks, with the easy familiarity permitted to wireless operators, and disappeared into his cabin.

The Skipper rang "Stand By" on the engine telegraph and brought the *Lincoln Star* broadside to the wind. "Finished with Engines." The bow wave diminished and the steady roll became a rocking. Instead of the swish outwards of foam on either side of the bows there was a quiet labial plashing of water against her smooth sides.

The *Knight of Castile*, another Grimsby trawler, was closer inshore. Against the dark cliffs of North Cape we had seen her turn to starboard, showing us all her length and the black expanse of her sail at the mainmast. She was bringing in her trawl.

The Skipper of the *Knight of Castile* was a bit of a lad, it was said. He was an enormous burly man and, when I heard his voice on the radio telephone, I pictured him with a red face and a beard, though whether or not he actually had these attributes I never discovered. All voices sound as though they come through a beard on a radio telephone in any case.

"Hallo, *Lincoln Star*! Hallo, *Lincoln Star*! Hallo, *Star*! *Star*! *Star*, *Star*! *Knight of Castile* calling, *Knight o' Castile*! *Knight o' Castile* calling *Lincoln Star*, *Knight* calling *Star*. . . ." The clear air between the two ships vibrated and quivered with his tremendous voice.

According to the stories that were told about "Smiler" Wraite of the *Knight of Castile*, he feared neither God nor man. He was one of the skippers who "poached" most frequently and most daringly and with the greatest measure of success around the Iceland coast.

It is forbidden, around the coast of Iceland as around all other coasts, to fish within the three mile territorial limit. The Danish Government employ several gunboats which patrol the coasts in order to see to it that trawlers do not fish within these limits. If any trawler is caught fishing within the forbidden zone there is awkwardness. The skipper is required to follow the gunboat back to Reykjavik where he is relieved of his entire catch and all his movable gear. No gear is left on his ship except such as may be required for her immediate safety, for mooring and for making fast. And the skipper is fined the value of his catch to date. Of course the trawler's crew are not particularly pleased at losing all their share of the catch but their displeasure is nothing to that of the owners who also lose their share of the catch and several hundred pounds' worth of valuable trawls, steel warps, head- and foot-ropes and so on. So the trawlers do not go poaching within the three mile limit if there is any likelihood that the gunboats, God damn them, are cruising in that part of the coast. But it is all very perplexing and difficult for the skippers because they say that the best fishing is to be found within the three mile limit close inshore. They would, perhaps, say that. But it is not entirely perversity on their part. Fishermen have a fish lore of their own and they know, from long and painful experience, where the best fish can be got and when. They know, for instance, that in the spring the best and largest cod are found, very often, close inshore, especially on the south side of the island. This is because the cod, the most important fish on the Iceland banks, spawns on the banks to the south of the island in the early months of the year about February and March in water between twenty and forty fathoms deep. This is most inconsiderate of them because a large part of the banks where they choose to spawn and shed their eggs, and where the water is between twenty and forty fathoms deep, lies inside that very zone where it is forbidden to catch them. Very fine catches of plaice, too, are often taken close inshore, for the plaice is a shallow water fish and feeds on the succulent molluscs that live in sandy and muddy shallows. So to a varying extent, dependent on their individual boldness, foolishness or canniness, or on the richness or poverty of the grounds outside, most of the skippers of all nationalities on the Iceland banks do, at some time or other, go poaching within the three mile limit. "Smiler" Wraite did this constantly and frequently, with the utmost boldness and with brilliant success. The Skipper of the *Lincoln Star* never did it. "I never take risks. It isn't necessary." For it is indeed a risky game. You play a game of Tom Tiddler's Ground with the gunboats. If you are caught you may, if the weather is sufficiently foul outside, say you were only sheltering. But then your gear and trawls must be correctly stowed inboard for sea otherwise the gunboat captain may politely insist, in spite of what you may say, that you have been guilty of the abominable crime of fishing in his waters. So before you venture across the forbidden line you find out, as discreetly as you can, from the other trawlers the whereabouts of the gunboats and what the chances are of their appearing suddenly out of the blue and catching you at it.

Only this last spring Skipper "Smiler" Wraite had been unable to bear the thought of all those fat cod shedding their eggs derisively in safety on the shallow banks within the limit on the southern coast. He was in another ship then, not in the *Knight of Castile*, and he had not had much luck with her. For ships differ a great deal. Some are lucky and you do well in them. Others are persistently unlucky. They hate you and you hate them. You do no good in them at all and nothing can be done about it. It is better to part company then for you know you will never get on. Skipper Wraite was not getting on with his ship. But he feared neither God nor man, as he constantly told everybody, and recognized no limits or barriers set up by the latter. What was the three mile limit to him, anyway? It was an imaginary thing drawn on a chart. You couldn't see it. There was nothing to stop you going over it. Anyhow he wasn't going to take things lying down from the old tub. Accordingly, hearing from other trawlers that only two of the gunboats were on patrol and that they were both, so far as was known, on the other side of the island, he crossed the three mile limit and steamed inshore to within twenty-five fathoms of water, right under the giant cliffs. Then he shot his trawl and

We had arrived upon our fishing grounds.

steamed seawards dragging it. After two hours' towing he brought it in and behold! what more could the heart desire? Over a hundred baskets of fine fat cod that flapped on to the deck gaping with stupid fishy astonishment at being thus taken unawares. This was nearly the quantity caught in four or five similar hauls outside, nearly a whole day's work. He put a dan buoy overboard at the place where he had brought in the trawl, so as to mark the spot, and steamed inshore again. A dan buoy is a buoyed flag or light anchored to the bottom so that it does not drift. When a trawler gets a good haul she marks the spot with a buoy such as this in order that she shall not lose touch with the rich ground through tide or set or drift. Skipper Wraite shot his trawl again under the frowning cliffs and steamed seawards once more, paying out more wire as the soundings deepened. The weather was calm and clear but the middle distance, some miles out to sea, was lost in a heightening bank of fog which advanced slowly upon the land.

The trawl had been down about an hour. Far to the westward along the coast a tiny speck appeared, plumed by a grey wisp of smoke.

"I think," said the Mate, "I think she's a gunboat."

The Skipper turned his glasses on the enlarging speck.

"Christ!" he said, and rang "Stand By."

Presently the telegraph rang "Finished with Engines."

"Heave up! And heave like hell—even if we lose the bloody gear!"

As the winches rattled and the warps came in the

distant speck enlarged under the line of cliffs. When the trawl came up the gunboat was plainly visible in every detail. She was steaming up to the trawler.

"Looks as though they've caught us this time," said the Skipper.

But the fog, advancing now like a writhing wall towards the shore, had almost overtaken the two ships. The gunboat was sometimes veiled now by wraiths of fog that detached themselves from the wall and slid across her bows.

The trawl came up and the bulging cod end hung swaying above the fore-deck, filled again with a fine haul of fat forbidden cod. The gunboat was running up signals. Then the fog ran in like a wall between the trawler and the gunboat cutting them off completely from one another. The trawler vanished like a ghost ship into the merciful veil that the Almighty, whom "Smiler" had so often disregarded, had drawn across his transgressions.

That was "Smiler's" closest shave. He had learnt from it a certain respect for the Almighty but none whatever for man. Now his great loud unrepentant voice could be heard booming and blaspheming in Sparks' little room. It spanned the mile or so of shining water between ourselves and the *Knight of Castile* with a bridge of noise.

"Hallo, *Lincoln Star*! Hallo, *Lincoln Star*! Hallo, *Star*! *Star*! Hallo, *Star*! *Knight o' Castile* calling! *Knight o' Castile* calling! No, laddie, there ain't much around here. Sooner I can get back to the White Sea the better I'll be pleased. Twelve baskets last haul and I've been buzzin' around these banks like a blue-arsed fly for four days now and I ain't got a hundred and fifty baskets yet. Not enough to feed the ship's cat! Well, laddie, we'll do our best. I'm hauling again in a minute or two. I'll let you know what I get. How's the missus and kids? Over."

"Over" meant "full stop," end of message, and with a click the splendid bridge of sound that Smiler had built across the space of sea snapped and crumbled into silence.

The *Knight of Castile* had come round broadside to the wind now in order to haul in her trawl. We could hear the winches rattling and see the steam of them rising on her deck. Soon we could make out the dark mass of the net alongside and the row of dark figures bending over her rail to grapple with it. Then again the distant rattle of her winches and we saw the cod end lifted up over the rail, hanging like a dark fruit, suspended for a moment or two above the fore-deck. Then the fruit collapsed, suddenly deflated, and the roaring voice came back and filled the bridge house, pouring out of Sparks' cabin in a torrent.

"Hallo, *Star*! Hallo, *Star*! *Castile* calling, *Castile*! Thought I'd just let ye know what I got before I send it aft for the cook to fry for the crew's tea!" And Gargantuan laughter came out of the brazen throat. "Bloody poor, laddie, bloody poor! About ten baskets, I should think—mostly small sprags. I'll try one more haul here and then beat it away east to Langanes. They're doin' better there by all accounts. S'long, laddie. Keep smilin'. Over!"

"Well," said the Skipper. "We'll have a shot. You never know. We might do better!"

The *Lincoln Star* lay also broadside to the wind. Nets are always shot and hauled with the ship lying thus so that she drifts away from them and there is no danger of the nets or gear fouling the screw.

The steel foot-rope with its row of spherical iron bobbins clanked over the rail and splashed into the water first. They lifted it by hauling upon two wire loops that were attached about a third of its length from each end. Wire hawsers, the jilsons, each ending in a hook, ran up over pulleys on the fore and main-mast derricks. They were taken to the outer axle drums of the main winches and wound upon them hand over hand.

"Jilson!" shouted Jim. Tom hooked the jilson into the forward loop on the foot-rope, and with swift deft movements he wound it three times round the axle drum of the winch. He pulled tight and the winch rattled. The fore jilson tightened so that the forward end of the great beaded necklace clanked up over the rail.

"Slack away on your jilson!" The forward bobbins splashed into the water over the side.

In the same way, using the after jilson on the main-mast, they lifted the after part of the foot-rope into the water.

They paid the net over into the water, hand over hand, standing in a row along the ship's rail to do it, Finally the head-rope, with its row of glass globes. floated like a beaded snake upon the surface. The net seemed transformed now into a huge submarine mouth gaping cavernously in the dim translucence with waving uncertain lips.

The winches clattered again and, from each gallows, the great ball-swivel that joins the foot-rope to the head-rope on either side of the mouth of the trawl slid shining into the water. This ball-swivel was always known as the " Dan Leno," though how that celebrated comedian had deserved so remarkable a monument I never found out. Now the iron-shod doors, the otter boards, hooked on to the main trawling wires, splashed down into the sea from the gallows fore and aft.

" Right! " shouted the Skipper, leaning over the bridge rail, " Ready? . . . Away then! " He rang " Full Speed Ahead." Now to the hiss and rattle of the winches the monstrous bag of netting fell away, faded and disappeared into the depths, a vast wavering mouth agape for prey. As the wires carried it out and down the little ship leapt forward and came wheeling round to starboard, splitting the white foam again. The wires, screaming out over the pulley blocks on the gallows, stretched and trembled with the strain they took and ripped through the water so that they tore from the surface little feathered fans where they cut it.

In her wake the *Lincoln Star* left a long curve of troubled water like a scimitar gleaming in the bright sunshine, and above it a hanging loop of smoke which spread and faded slowly.

In this way the trawl was shot every one of the fifty or more times they shot it during the trip. All of them on board the *Lincoln Star*, except Jack Johnson perhaps, who was a learner, had shot the trawl so many hundreds of times that they went through all the movements almost automatically. They had become very nearly reflex movements like those of walking or eating. And yet it is not so simple a business as it looks. Anything done supremely well is so much more difficult than it seems to be. For so many things may happen during the shooting of the trawl which may be disastrous to the trawl or even, possibly, to the ship. The trawl may sink belly upwards, or the wires may becomes twisted over one another, or the after wire may become foul of the propellers. In order to pay the net away fairly over the side the ship is always brought up broadside to the wind so that she drifts away from the net while it is being shot. When the net is fairly over the side and the warps are paid out the ship goes full speed ahead with the helm hard a-starboard and the wires carry the net out and away clear of the screw. That is, if the starboard trawl is being used. If the port trawl is being used she goes ahead with the helm to port.

This is the one thrilling, exhilarating moment of the trawl. I never missed it. For the little ship, sweeping round in a splendid arc, the smoke streaming from her funnel, seemed to be filled suddenly with a trembling life and eagerness, like a racehorse. There was a sense of gigantic strain, a quiver from stem to stern, and a light in the eyes of the men as they shouted "Away she goes!"

The two main trawling wires, hauling the otter boards over the fore and after gallows, were marked off by means of rope pads into twenty fathom lengths. They paid out a length of trawling wire equal to three times the depth of the sea. Since we were trawling in about ninety fathoms they paid out from the winches, on this first occasion, about two hundred and eighty fathoms of wire. When Jim and Tom at the two winches had paid out that length of wire, watching steadily the rope pads follow one another off the drums, round the deck fair-leads and up over the gallows into the sea in a long even procession, they clanked on the winch brakes and shouted up to the bridge, " All away, Skipper! " Then the two trembling taut wires were clamped together aft of the after gallows with an iron clamp level with the ship's rail so as to keep the forward trawling wire up clear of the hull when the ship swung to the helm.

The Skipper rang " Half Speed " on the engine telegraph and the quivering eager charge forward of the *Lincoln Star* was over. The bow wave diminished again and the water lapped past gently, glimmering in the sunshine, as she settled down to her steady towing speed, two knots.

" Well," said the Skipper, standing on the bridge and gazing down at the wires that shook with the strain of the trawl dragging along the bottom more than five hundred feet below, " We'll see if we get anything. We'll tow for three hours and see what we get. Keep her south thirty-five west, Jake."

" South thirty-five west. Yurss, Skipper."

" Nice cup o' tea," said the Sergeant as the men trooped into the galley to fill their china mugs. " What you want's a nice cup o' tea after that. I made a fresh kettle."

" What d'ye think to this fishin' now, lad? Bloody mug's game, ain't it? "

" Soon be home now and I'll have a little bit put

by towards that bike. Don't forget now, what you said about comin' to see me."

"I got to get a new old woman. That's what I got to do."

"I got to get some sleep," said Tom.

CHAPTER X

" CALL out, Skipper? "

" Aye, call out, Tom."

Tom left the wheel and went for'ard under the cluster lights that were slung along the fore-deck to call out the sleeping hands again. His elongated shadow overtook him along the rail, disappeared, reformed behind him and overtook him again as he went. In the darkness of the fo'c'sle the entrance to the companion way was a faintly lit rectangle which Tom's figure obscured for a second as he entered. Soon, one by one, they came out on deck into the star-shine, some pulling on caps, others tying their cloths around their necks, others adjusting the string that bound the sleeves of their oilskins around their wrists. They were all wearing yellow oilskins that pulled in one piece over their heads, for bringing in the trawl is a soaking wet job and it is better not to wear anything that has buttons on it, for men have sometimes been pulled over the side by the buttons catching in a run-away bight of the net.

The trawl had been down and up again some four or five times since we had first shot it when we arrived on the banks that bright morning twelve hours ago. But they had had no luck for on each occasion, after three hours' haul, it had come in with nothing better than a few small cod and a great quantity of those scarlet fish known as soldiers, all of which were swept scornfully back into the sea as so much trash.

"Somebody ain't paid for his washin' in Blyth," they said. When luck is bad at sea sailors say that somebody on board has sailed from port without paying his laundry bill and has provoked the fury of the powers by this unpardonable offence.

But at this time of the year, the Skipper said, you never know your luck. You may strike a rich patch suddenly so it is better not to give up and waste time steaming away to other grounds which might be no better than this one. No one was doing much good by all accounts. It was better to stick around and keep on trying until you struck lucky. And keep your ears open and don't tell anything. "Some skippers spend all their time talking," he said. "No one learns anything from me."

Now it was nearly midnight. The sky was filled with stars which stood again in an inky sea that heaved a little, making invisible things clink and rattle gently on the deck. The smoke from the funnel made a high dark band of shadow, blotting out an alley through the stars. The other trawlers had become constellations of light here and there around us. Slowly they changed their shape and position against the loom of the mountains southwards.

During the hours through which we steamed slowly round, towing the straining trawling wires, the men had slept below when they could. And no one had spoken on the bridge for a long time. Tom's cigarette glowed behind the wheel and the Skipper, leaning upon the bridge window, hummed a rag-time song gently to himself. Sometimes he said, "Well, it's a grand night for it," or "Wonder if we'll get anything this time. Think I'll steam eastwards a bit if we don't." I stayed on the bridge gazing at the star-filled sea. I wanted to see a good haul before I turned in, although I knew I should see the trawl come in many times before the trip was over. I knew I should be sick of the sight long before the end. Sometimes I went aft with the tea mugs and filled them from the galley kettle. The galley was silent and deserted. Pans and pots and long-handled spoons swung on their hooks awaiting the morning return of their master, who had long ago finished his game of solo in the saloon and had turned in. But the stove was still bright with the kettle hissing comfortably upon it. I could help myself with impunity and without offence.

In his little cabin off the bridge Sparks was hanging his head over a book while the air all about him was filled with voices. Cheerful, jocular, blasphemous, optimistic, pessimistic, they filled the night air as full as they filled the air of high noon with the hopes and fears that wait on fishermen. Only occasionally Sparks lifted his head from the book, pushed back his lock of hair, and listened, his face suddenly intent to catch what was being said out of the metal throat above him. Sometimes, without raising his eyes from the page, he stretched out his hand and turned a knob, cutting off one voice and letting in another like a flood. And now and then the Skipper left the bridge window to lean in the cabin doorway listening.

"Hallo, *Lancastrian* ! Hallo, *Lancastrian* ! How're ye doin'? Pretty rotten here. Been around Grimsey all day long. Sweet F.A. my lad. That's what I got.

About fifteen baskets o' small sprags last haul. Dunno what's happened to the ruddy fish. Must be gettin' wise I reckon. Seen us comin', I shouldn't wonder! Well, s'long. Over!"

But Sparks kept his eyes on the page. The books that he read with such avidity stood on the little shelf above his bunk in an orderly and somehow respectful row. They were waiting patiently and respectfully, as is the way of books, to transport their owner, whenever he felt inclined, into a land of high romance and adventure. They held the key of the gate. At a movement of the arm, up to the shelf, and another of the hand, to turn the page, those gates would be instantly unlocked. "I must say," said Sparks, "I do like a bloody good read," much as one might say "I do like a good bath," or "a good glass of beer." While the ship circled slowly, rocking from side to side, or pitching and staggering in a gale, or hooting in a blank fog, Sparks performed acts of gallantry to a young lady wearing a leopard skin and a permanent wave on a deserted coral island. Or did the work of six men up aloft in imaginary rigging. Or said, "You leave the kid alone, you great bully!" directing a well-aimed blow at the chin of a bullying, but happily imaginary, second mate. For he read nothing but sea stories of the simpler and more ingenuous sort written by people who knew more about ships than about the men who sailed in them. One adventure particularly enthralled him and, when I had run out of things to read and had been through several old cheap weeklies from cover to cover, he lent it to me.

"Damn fine yarn," he said. "You'll enjoy that."

The hero was cast away in an open boat for six weeks in the tropics with the delicately nurtured young heroine. All the courtesies and conventions were mostly strictly observed.

"What I want to know, Sparks," I said, "is, how did they? So far as I can make out neither of them ever did."

"Bloody 'ell," said Sparks, really shocked. "You would think of a thing like that!"

But every now and then Sparks wrenched himself back from these delights in order to listen to the voices that never ceased shouting into his ear. It seemed as though he reserved some corner of his brain for them which kept watch and every now and then said, "Come on! Listen!" Then his head would go up and remain turned a little sideways listening, a look of sudden attention on his face.

"Skipper! *Golden Spur* got a haul of eighty baskets round the east side off Seydisfjördur. Been there four days, he says, but this is the first time he's got owt!"

"Try and find out what the others are doing on the east side."

"Right-oh, Skip!"

And, with his hands busy upon the dials of his instrument, his eyes were already on the page again, picking up the threads where he had just dropped them. "Her girlish innocence was a constant solace to the rough sailors and, above their rude jests, her tinkling laughter. . . ."

"Right!" said the Skipper, "heave up."

Jim at the winches, the electric lights gleaming

upon his oilskins, turned the steam valves and the wires began running in on to the winch drums again. The ship was stationary now and broadside to the wind once more so that a little flurry of tiny choppy waves stippled the dark water along her sides. The rope pads, spaced along the trawling wires at twenty fathom intervals, ran in over the gallows pulley blocks in a long steady procession, moving up to the rhythm of the winches, up out of the darkness and down over the fair-leads. The whole ship vibrated with the even pulse and throb of the winches winding in the hundreds of feet of wire. Presently the great rectangles of the otter boards burst through the surface gleaming, the forward one first and then the after one. Cataracts of foam streamed off them as they clattered up to the gallows. The winches stopped and the boards hung at the gallows dripping while the deckies unhooked them from the wires. They hung the boards upon the gallows and the winches turned again, more slowly and gently now, as the "Dan Lenos" came in. Their round surfaces shone dully. When they too had come up to the gallows pulley blocks the winches stopped.

If now you leant over the rail of the bridge-deck and peered into the darkness below you could see dimly beneath the surface the head-rope with its line of glass globes like beads. And below that the great gaping open mouth of the trawl.

The head-rope was brought in first and made fast. The trawl lay now like a curtain over the side of the ship, wet and dripping, an inert shapeless mass with little limp dead things, fragments of jelly or of marine undergrowth, tiny fish, caught in its meshes. The men stood over it in a long row along the rail armed with S-shaped hooks of iron. They dug their hooks into the mass of wet netting on the rail and, at the word from Jim, they leant backwards together and heaved.

" Come on, men! All together, heave! Hup! And again, hup! "

All together they leant back in a row and pulled. A foot or so of net came in slowly over the rail. It is a soaking wet business this and the men wear oilskins for it even in the warmest weather. It is not without its risks too. Last year Tom had been pulled into the water by the weight of the net running away suddenly over the rail when the men let go of it. In heavy weather, with the ship lying thus broadside on, big seas often come over the rail so that the men work knee and sometimes waist deep. Jim broke a rib two seasons ago when a sea threw him against the casing as they were bringing in the trawl.

" And again, men. Heave-hup! "

" Come up, ye bastard! "

They heaved together in a row, leaning back simultaneously on their iron hooks so that foot by foot they hauled the inert mass of netting inboard over the rail. It seemed to come sluggishly and unwillingly. It is astonishing how much mere folds of waterlogged net can weigh. As many hands were wanted for this game as it was possible to get so I heaved with them if I could find a spare S-hook lying about anywhere. They stuck in their hooks with savage grunts as though they were digging into the flesh of an enemy.

" And again, men! Hey-up, heave! "

Presently so much of the net had been hauled in thus hand over hand that only the narrower end of the bag of the trawl lay in the sea. All the wide mouth and the back and belly of it lay piled in a wet heap upon the deck along the rail. Now they got a rope strop round the narrow waist of the net and heaved it up with the jilson.

In the dark water about twenty feet from the ship's side an oily smooth dome arose slowly, creaming upwards from below like a submarine fountain. In the middle of it the cod end of the trawl pushed up like the snout of an animal. You could see the curved backs of the entrapped fish gleaming within it. A gaping mouth or a bulging eye stuck through the meshes here and there.

When this snout pushed up through the water they paused in their hauling on the waist of the net.

" Not much bleedin' good, that lot! " they said after a moment's silence.

" Christ Almighty! " said the Skipper, gazing down at the protuberant cod end from the bridge deck. " What the hell's the good of that? "

For we could see now that there was little in the cod-end. The snout of it rising in the water was thin and pointed instead of being round and bulging as it would be if it were full, and as it broke the surface and the smooth dome around it spread and disappeared, a circle of escaped fish widened upon the surface of the sea. Again they were " soldiers " in their scarlet jackets. Their eyes bulged like headlamps, their guts projected from their mouths. And you knew

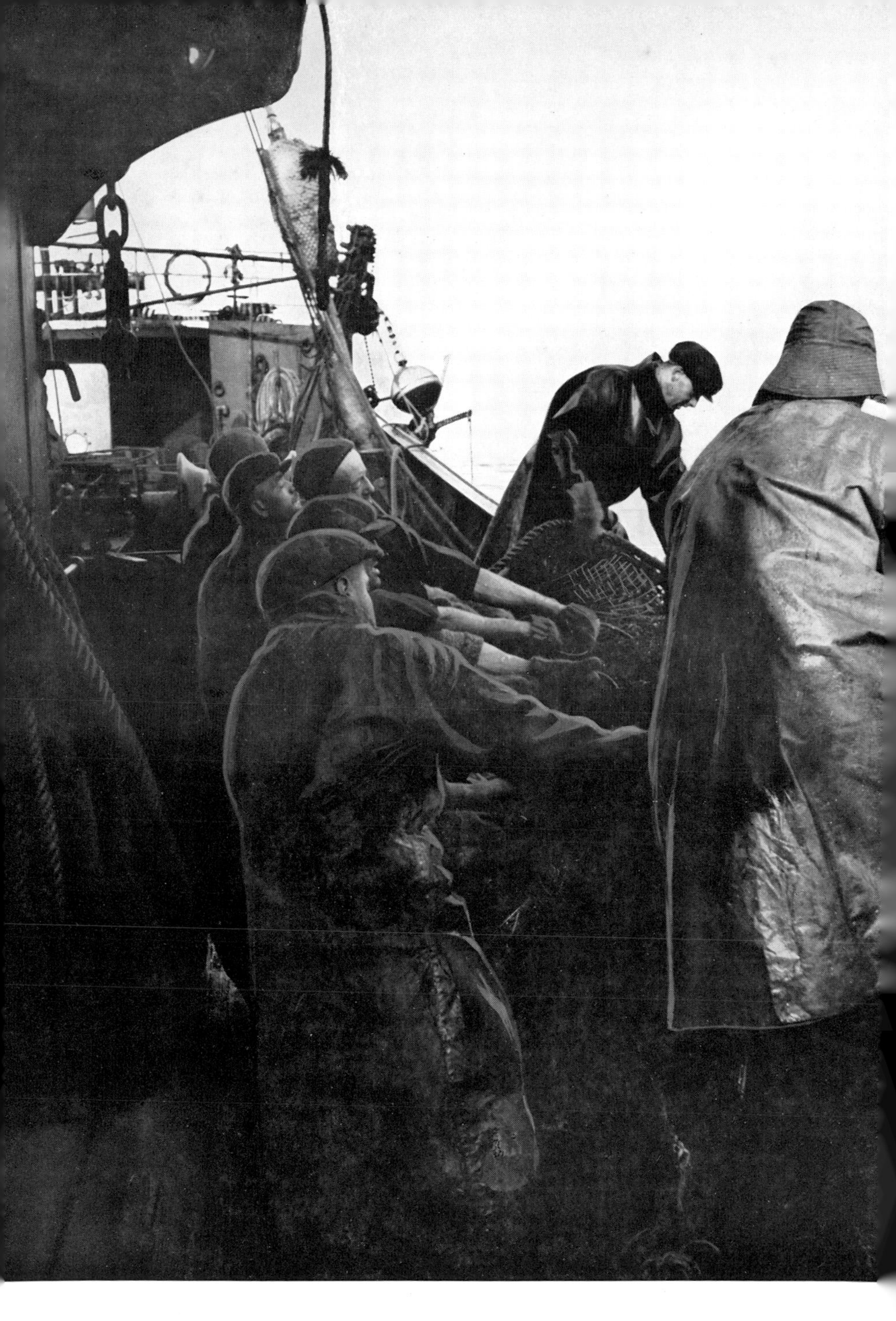

"And again, men. Heave!"

that if you got a large catch of " soldiers " you would get nothing else besides. Sometimes, when the fishing was bad or towards the end of a trip, the trawlermen might keep the largest " soldiers " for they are not bad fish and may reach a foot and a half in length. But not at this early stage of the fishing. They floated away on the black sea in a widening arc, those that had escaped through the meshes, lying upon their sides and making occasional feeble fluttering movements to get themselves down again to the familiar depths from which they had been so ruthlessly torn away.

They hove the cod-end up with the forward jilson and it hung like a great dripping fruit, like a fig, above the fore-deck, swinging to the movement of the ship. The Bo'sn, stooping beneath it in the rain of drops, untied the rope slip-knot below it and it disgorged itself upon the deck, vomiting out a flapping, slithering, gaping multitude.

" Fat lot o' good that is! " said the Skipper. " I think we'd better steam east a bit."

For it was a red-coated army of "soldiers" that flopped out on to the deck, some a foot or so long but mostly small and all useless. And there was a spongy, slimy mass of growths, " trash," all of which would be swept back into the sea.

" Hallo, *Lincoln Star*! Hallo, *Star*! Saw you bring yer trawl in jest now! How're ye doin', laddie? Any luck? Over! "

Sparks jerked himself back from the China Seas, or from the terrace of the Raffles Hotel, or from the palm-fringed shores of Tahiti. The great voice of " Smiler " Wraite was bellowing in his ear again.

At once his face assumed the look of intentness and attention.

" *Knight of Castile* speaking to you, Skip. Wants to know what luck."

" Luck, hell! " said the Skipper. " Tell 'im I'm busy on the fore-deck."

CHAPTER XI

This is the point where I find myself compelled to take notice of the lump that had for several days, throughout the whole trip in fact, been lying just under my diaphragm. It was a familiar thing. I have been conscious of it more or less all my life as though it were a kind of tumour. But years and months might pass during which I forgot about it until suddenly something occurred to irritate or aggravate it so that it became a great heavy thing like a cyst lying just under the heart. It was fear.

The first occasion upon which I became conscious of my cyst was at school, I think. On my first day there I was standing, miserable and utterly lonely, under the chestnut tree in the quadrangle, wishing I had never been born.

"Hallo! Here's a stinking new bug. What's your name?"

A face covered with freckles under a shock of red hair was pushed close to mine. I looked into a pair of pale fishy eyes with colourless lashes and said my name.

"Good God! What a name and a half! What do they call you at home?"

I knew this for an old and well worn trap, of course.

"Dick."

"O-o-w, ow! Look at it—darling little Dickie! Gosh! You bloody sickening little wart!"

I had said good-bye to my parents only half an hour ago. With the heart-breaking memory of that parting, which seemed as though it were to be for ever, still in my mind I did an unpremeditated and, for me, astonishing thing. I dashed my infantile hand full into the fish-like face that was pushed malevolently so close to mine. I remember the stupefied expression that came over it during that second, to be succeeded immediately by one of terrifying malignity. But I was saved from an awful and immediate vengeance by the appearance of the headmaster, vague and preoccupied, advancing in the distance from the door in the quadrangle.

"You wait," said two or three voices together in an undertone. "You just wait, by God! Just you wait till we get you in the dorm to-night. We don't take that from stinking new bugs. It'll be the gauntlet for you."

And they vanished.

"Well, my boy," said the Head benignly, his hand on my shoulder. "Making friends already, I see. That's good. These are the happiest days of your life, you know. Make the most of them, make the most of them."

"Yessir."

He limped away across the quadrangle, his shabby gown slipping from his shoulders.

It was then that I became conscious of my cyst for the first time.

The dormitory was a long garret of a room in an old part of the building which prided itself on its age but had little to offer beside. It had no conveniences of any sort. There was no lavatory or bathroom, so far as I can remember, within less than about a quarter of an hour's walk of the dormitory. There were no heating arrangements and the whole gaunt room was lit by one bubbling gas bracket. Every morning, summer and winter, about sixteen skinny half-naked figures advanced upon basins of cold water, shivering, their arms crossed upon their hairless chests. In winter the water in the basins was solid ice. Whether we were being hardened or educated by this process I do not know but I have no doubt it made us what we all now are.

There were eight hard little white beds down each side of this room. Along one side were windows with diamond panes through which, as I lay in bed, I could see the stars above the terribly Elizabethan castellated roof and twisted chimneys. I could see the great chestnut tree with its thousands of candelabra in the summer-time. And through a bow window at the end of the room I could see the cedar trees in the headmaster's garden waving tapered fingers and entangling the moon and evening star.

The dormitory was ruled over by a prefect whose authority was like that of a Roman Emperor or a Greek Tyrant. Sometimes he was playful and indulgent, familiar with his subjects, and then, at the next moment, he was the ruthless and bullying potentate, dealing out fearful punishment without question and frequently without justification.

"You! Come and see me in the lower sixth to-morrow morning at ten o'clock."

"But, Mayhew, I never——"

" Shut up! If you don't keep your mouth shut I'll give you a dozen instead of six."

This capricious deity made a state entry into the dormitory, very grandly, hands in pockets, half an hour after his subjects, all of whom were expected to be in their beds by the time he arrived. But in that half-hour of licence the subjects settled their own scores. It was then that unpopular members of the dormitory—usually new boys whose only offence, as a rule, was that they were new—were submitted to a variety of refined and satisfying tortures. The gauntlet was one of them.

It was decided by common consent who was to run the gauntlet, and why and when. In other words, the dominating character in the dormitory said, " I vote we make So-and-so run the gauntlet to-night for bloody sauce. Any one not agree? " And no one dared to disagree. In any case it was a pleasant sadistic pastime. So the dormitory lined up in two rows, clad only in their pyjama trousers, each man armed with a wet knotted face towel. So-and-so was made to run between the two rows while they lashed at his bare back with the towels. It was fun. It was sadistic and it was forbidden. Two terms ago a whole dormitory had been beaten by the Head for doing it so you usually stationed a new bug at the door to keep " cave."

In the interval between supper and prayers they told me all the details and described the process so graphically that it became obvious to me that I should be lucky if I survived that night. And when voices hissed into my ear, "You wait! It's the gauntlet for you!" I was unashamedly and unrestrainedly afraid. A great lump came and settled under my diaphragm. During prayers I said, "Don't let them make me run the gauntlet. Don't let them!"

The lump was turning over like a mill wheel as I slowly and fearfully undressed. And then, suddenly and surprisingly, the door opened and the prefect walked in, by a miracle half an hour too early, and began to undress too. "Gosh!" he said, "I'm fagged out. Been in the train all day." I slid into my little bed, grateful for one night's respite anyway, and, curling myself up into a ball, pretended to be asleep.

"What d'you think of the new bugs, Mayhew?" I heard my fish-faced enemy ask.

"Can't say I've studied them much," said Mayhew loftily.

"Well, have a look at that bloody little wart over there."

"What about him?"

"It's a stinker—and I owe it one for sauce."

"Oh, leave the kid alone for Christ's sake! You're not such a beefer yourself, so far as I remember, when you've got the gloves on."

This stinging retort referred to an occasion when my enemy had failed lamentably to distinguish himself in a boxing tournament last term. It was followed by an abashed and horrified silence. Listening under the bedclothes I heard a faint titter run round the dormitory and knew that I was saved. I never ran the gauntlet but lived to administer it to somebody else with great gusto in my second term. Small boys are horrible little savages and I was no better than any others.

So my cyst died down.

But it has reappeared on several subsequent occasions during my life and I felt it again, and knew it for what it was, when I settled in my corner at King's Cross station on that dull September morning.

" Well," said the big man in the far corner, arranging himself and his overcoat. " It looks pretty serious now. I'm afraid we're for it."

The lump under my diaphragm turned over like a mill wheel. I was going to run the gauntlet after all.

I went through my emotional crisis about war several years ago when I first realized, with a sort of horrified shock, that this world of radios, football pools, patent medicines, deferred payments and all-singing, all-talking, all-screaming entertainment is neither permanent nor immovable, and is not necessarily the goal towards which mankind has been moving for two thousand years since the birth of Christ. It is liable, I discovered with stupefaction, to be blown sky high by forces of its own generation. So I had got all that part of it over and on that September morning, as the train rattled north through Hertfordshire, I do not remember being filled with any particular emotion at the prospect of the ruin of what the weeklies call " our civilization and all that it stands for." Nor was I whipped into fury at the thought that large numbers of people in other countries have decided that Democracy is not quite all that we crack it up to be. It is only natural,

I thought, that they should show a certain lack of restraint in proclaiming the discovery.

I am not ashamed to say that what I chiefly felt in the train going north through the jerry builders' paradise of Hertfordshire, through the featureless miles of Lincolnshire, dull beneath a pall of grey, was physical fear. It is a common complaint and it takes with me a definite physical form of a lump under my diaphragm. That which I had shut out of my mind for so long and refused to contemplate was towering above me darkening the sky. It was towering above every man, woman and child I set eyes on at the stations and from the windows of the train. But even so there still remained a little bit of my mind shut against this thing. A bus gliding over a bridge as the train shot beneath, a woman seen for an instant shaking her mat at a back door, an errand boy glimpsed for an instant zig-zagging down a quiet side street, all the familiar and pleasurable glimpses of a railway journey combined to say to me, " No, impossible! " They strove to close the doors of my mind against it.

But, nevertheless, there was the fat man in the corner, crackling his Sunday newspaper and saying portentously, " It's damned serious. We're for it all right."

I could not imagine these people, the dining-car attendants, the young woman quietly reading *Appointment in Samarra* at the next table, the fatherly guard, the porters and the three comfortable ladies who got in at Peterborough, lashed into the fever of excitement and hot patriotism that I remembered dimly from twenty years go. My father had said, "Plucky little Belgium! Well done! Well done!" and sat for a long time staring out of the window. But somehow or other they would have to be so lashed. I wanted to say to everybody, "Don't you realize how serious this is?" To the young woman placidly reading, "What's the good of your sitting there reading about a small town in middle-west America, and an imaginary one at that, when your own world is going up in smoke and horror almost at any moment." Perhaps, however, she was wiser than I was.

"Will you take the sweet or cheese, sir?"

The young attendant's face was white and spotty from indigestion, lack of fresh air and lack of healthy exercise. But it was a pleasant face. I wanted to tell him that something terrible was about to happen to him. "You're going to be blown to bits—and quite soon. But before that happens you're going to get good food, fresh air and healthy exercise. They'll make you into a fine, strong, handsome boy so that your girl won't know you. And then they'll blow you to bits." But I knew he would probably think I was mad and might even call the guard and have me removed from the train as a dangerous lunatic. So I said:

"Cheese, please—and some biscuits and butter."

At Peterborough three stout old women got in with suitcases and crackling parcels. They seemed to spend an eternity revolving on their own axes in the middle of the compartment, arranging suitcases on racks and under seats, distributing parcels, treading on toes and making of themselves a general, kindly, genial and forgivable nuisance. They trod on the toes of the man who said the situation was serious and said they were sorry they were sure. Finally they came to rest like large coloured tops at the end of their spin and sat beaming opposite one another, their comfortable bosoms heaving with so much exertion. They had kind housewifely grey eyes and the mild rosy faces of Lincolnshire country folk.

"Would this be right for Great Grimsby?" they said in slightly anxious voices.

"Yes, quite right."

They composed themselves, their parcels crackling slightly on their laps. The situation and the seriousness thereof meant nothing to them. The future was for them a long succession of simple days filled with familiar tasks, cooking, washing up, mending, buying groceries, feeding chickens. And their chief and overshadowing anxiety had been lifted by the nice young gentleman in the corner who seemed, however, a bit depressed about something or other. They were right for Great Grimsby.

The day before the *Lincoln Star* sailed Hitler made at Nuremburg the speech for which the world had been waiting in a state of tense anxiety for several days. In the bar of the *Crown* in Riby Square, Grimsby, they were not impressed.

"Opened 'is mouth and ain't said nowt," said the man with the bowler hat and the glasses. He put down his pint of dark and pointed his finger at the barman. "D'you know what I bloody well think?"

" No, what? "

" Bluff. All bleedin' bluff. That's what it is. If we was to stand up to 'im now——"

The barman set the half-pint I had ordered on the bar in front of me and then leaned across the bar towards the man in the bowler hat. He seemed about to reveal some astonishing intelligence, to let the man in the bowler hat in on some exclusive and private piece of information that would explain everything and set all doubts at rest. He was a small thin young man with dark eyes that blazed with the fever of conviction.

" D'you know what *I* think? " he said as though challenging all comers, daring them to say they did not want to hear what he thought. " There's only one man who wants a war. One man only! " And he straightened himself at the bar and polished it vigorously with his cloth.

" Who's that? " I asked, unwilling to let him down.

" Chamberlain! "

So astonishing and unorthodox a view silenced everybody at the bar. The man in the bowler hat, his beer half-way to his lips, put his glass down again and gaped.

" No! You don't think that? Honest? "

" Sure I do. Him and his Cabinet. They want war. They want it all right. 'Course they do."

" Why do you say that? " I said.

" Well, so's they can make a bit out of it o' course. And then retire and live in the country and have big houses and fancy women all round them and servants in uniform."

Then I felt that the situation was really beyond me so deep was the conviction in his flashing dark eyes. But so engaging was the picture and so romantic the thought of our Machiavellian Cabinet Ministers living in oriental splendour, like caliphs and sultans, on the misery and subjection of their people, that I burst out laughing. It was the most unkind reply I could have made for the little barman went sorrowfully away.

"Nobody wants it here," said a voice. I turned and saw a gaunt thin elderly man sitting at a table with a glass of beer before him. He was shabbily dressed but his speech was that of an educated man and a southerner. He wiped his forehead with a handkerchief. "I'm waiting for the proprietor," he continued, apparently feeling it very necessary to explain his presence. "Otherwise I wouldn't be here. I don't go into bars very often but I've got business with the proprietor so I thought I'd just have a beer while I wait." All this was said very apologetically as though it were an inexcusable moral lapse on his part to have a beer in a pub. "But I couldn't help overhearing what you gentlemen were saying. No, no one wants it here. And I don't think there are many over there want it either. In my way of business I've a good deal to do with the German trawlermen that come over here. I'm agent for some of their ships. You couldn't want a finer lot of men. They don't want war. They want to be left alone. That's what we all want. We want to be left alone. Life's hard enough in these parts without all that." He finished his beer apologetically.

"Have another," I said.

" Oh no! Oh, thank you, no! I wouldn't be here except that I've got business with the proprietor. I don't often come into bars. But I've been quite a bit in Germany too. D'you know Germany at all by any chance? "

" Yes," I said. " I've been there several times."

The little group in the bar, the young barman with the burning eyes, the man in the bowler hat, one or two faded people at the tables, became suddenly interested in me. Here was a fairly ordinary looking person who had actually been to Germany where they shoot you on sight, where they walk about with their arms permanently raised above their heads in a state of frenzied salutation, where everyone does the goose step in the street, where they beat women and children with rubber truncheons, where they murder and destroy, where they fall down and worship a man with a tooth-brush moustache like Charlie Chaplin, where all the people evidently have tails and wear loin cloths. This young man sat there and said, astonishingly, " Yes, I've been there several times."

Perhaps I had had too much beer, that and the consciousness that I had an audience who were looking to me for some sort of a statement about something. An audience has a fatal effect upon me. Before I face it my knees knock together and my spirits fail. I feel the cyst beneath my diaphragm. But once on my feet before them an electrifying change occurs. I find myself saying all kinds of things that can, as a rule, only be written. It is not so much that the floodgates are opened, letting forth a spate of eloquence, as that a desire overcomes me to cut some sort of a figure before all those people. This desire to cut a figure, before the tired man who seldom went into pubs, the man in the bowler hat, the young barman and the faded people at the tables, overwhelmed me now, aided by several pints of dark ale.

For this reason, because I was drunk or because I wanted to show off, I told them, somewhat obscurely I am afraid, about the little town of Schleussingen in the Harz mountains where we came one summer evening a year or so ago. A great grey castle brooded over the town and the dark forest hung like a heavy curtain all around, fretting the margin of the sunset. There was a fountain dripping quietly in the centre of a square of little gabled houses, and a rococo town hall, I think, supporting itself upon pillars. When our car drew up before the one hotel in the square a little woman with grey hair and spectacles ran out and made us welcome. She superintended the unstrapping of our luggage with her hands folded beneath her black satin bosom, beaming gently through her spectacles.

"*Ausländer, nicht war?*"

"Yes," we said. "English."

"*Engländer? Ach, wirklich? Aber dass ist etwas sehr interessantes.*" And she lifted both her hands, leaning backwards and filling the quiet square with peals of delighted laughter. Her husband, bald and bearded, stood in the background smiling and leaning upon a stick. A boy and a girl carried our luggage up to little rooms, cleaner and sweeter than any I had ever seen before. The bare boards were scrubbed white, the linen on the beds was spotless and a resinous breeze from the mountains blew aside the coloured curtains that hung before the windows.

"*Es ist hübsch*," said the girl simply, putting my suitcase on the floor. Both she and her brother had that veiled look in their grey eyes that so many Germans have. They did the work of the house, the girl cooking, under the supervision of her mother, with the help of one or two other equally buxom girls, and the boy waiting in the dining-room and in the café and doing odd jobs such as cleaning shoes, carrying trunks, scrubbing floors and so on. Whenever we wanted anything we walked into the great brick-floored kitchen and asked for it in our appalling German. "*Wollen sie, bitte, ein wenig heisses Wasser aufbringen?*" Whereupon we were greeted by screams of unashamed laughter while they both fell over themselves to do our bidding, punching and pummelling each other whenever they got in each other's way. On one occasion I called down from the top of the stairs for some hot water and they both rushed at the stairs together carrying ewers, collided and stuck there helpless with laughter while the hot water ran away over the floor.

We ate in the evening under the trees outside in the square. Little fair-haired boys and girls collected to watch us, round-eyed with astonishment. Some of them had bicycles and they bicycled round and round the square, staring and laughing every time they passed us. Some of the cleverer ones showed off for our benefit and went swooping past without holding on to the handle-bars or with their feet up on the front mudguard and the pedals spinning regardless.

We clapped and shouted, "*Gut! Wunderbar!*" Then a man in brown with a shaven head and a swastika on his arm came and chased the pretty children away, leaving nothing for us to look at but the fountain dripping gently.

It's a mad world. One day I shall go back to Schleussingen again. When we left, having stayed several days instead of the one we meant to stay, the old lady said, "*Kommen sie bald wieder.*" And I will.

"Time, gentlemen, please!"

"I'm sorry," I said. "I'm afraid I've been talking too much. But those are the things I remember at times like these. I shut my mind to all the rest. One should only judge by one's own experience anyway. Good-night to you."

"Well, I'm glad to hear you say that. That's just what I always think. I'm glad to have met you. Stroke of luck really because I wouldn't be here only I had business with the proprietor. I don't often go into bars. . . ."

I took this bogey away to sea with me. The impending doom was all about us in the air even off the lonely coast of Iceland, in thick fog or driving rain, or in the calm blue days that shone suddenly, without warning, through the pall of cloud. It was shouted from ship to ship. Great genial voices proclaimed calamity whenever Sparks switched on the radio telephone.

". . . . What a world, eh? What a world, lad! Just think what one man can do to it too. . . ."

" . . . . Well, I suppose we'll have to go and give 'em a hand! Have to call in the old 'uns like you an me, Bill, when things go wrong! . . ."

" . . . . Looks like it's comin' now. The Czechs have mobilized. Germans have sent 'em a bleedin' ultimatum or summat. You know, hand over or we knock your block off kind o' style! . . . "

But the voices had no fear or doubt in them. They gave you courage somehow. Whatever the future might bring they faced it, the old 'uns. And through it all, unruffled and unconcerned, Sparks kept his eyes upon his book. In his imagination he was far away from it all in happier climes, in the world of fiction which is still brave and romantic, peopled by God-like figures, and not yet mad and at bursting point like a steam engine with no safety valve. I felt an unworthy longing to rouse Sparks out of it, to jolt him back into the hideous world in which I was living myself, the real world which you could touch and see and feel but which seemed too fantastic to be true.

We listened several times a day to the radio bulletins in Sparks' little cabin, the Skipper, I and Sparks and sometimes the Bo'sn or Jim. When the grave voice finished on each occasion we stood staring at each other for a bit, saying nothing.

"Well," I would say presently, feeling that the silence must be filled. "It's a nice state of things, isn't it?"

"Aye, it looks pretty serious now," the Skipper would answer. "How's her head, Jake?"

"North fifteen East."

"Oh, bloody 'ell," Sparks would say and would be

back instantly to his own romantic world, his long forelock hanging over the page once more.

But it was a fairly long time before our little community properly understood the meaning of it all. The deckies heard no news bulletins. During the first few days of the trip Sparks typed out the news and gave them the typewritten sheet to read at midday dinner next day. But at the end of the first week the Skipper forbad it. " They don't want to worry about that," he said. " Let 'em keep their minds on their work." So they heard only indirectly, from fragments brought down to them by the helmsman when he came off watch, from stray bits of talk or from answers to direct questions, what was happening in their absence to the outer world and what might become of all those plans they had made for their return. And when at last the cloud began to darken their skies also I was able to observe, in the saloon or in the deckies' mess-room, their separate and individual reactions.

" Well, if it comes to anything, like," said Jim, "—mind you, I don't say it will but if it should do—I think I'll be sending my little family away to my sister in Fleetwood. Her husband's in a job up there, see. Then they'll be all right, in a manner of speaking, if anything should happen to me. . . ."

" I'm sure that would be the best thing to do, Jim."

It was typical and right and natural that for Jim the prospect of war meant nothing whatsoever apart from its impact upon his little family, his wife and children. The death and torture of millions, the putting out of all light in the world was for him condensed down to just that private calamity. It is so for most of us. To only a few, perhaps, is it given to feel a larger part of the general suffering of mankind.

The Sergeant, however, saw things in a very different light. It was the impact of war upon himself personally that was his immediate concern. On the day when the clouds were at their darkest and the worst seemed almost certain the Sergeant wore a clean white coat and apron and a cook's cap. It was only Wednesday, three days before the orthodox time for such a change. He stood to attention when each one of us came into the saloon and saluted, fixed bayonets with a carving knife and plunged it deep into a steak pie as though into the bowels of an enemy.

"At the stomach—point! Aye, that's me. Back again. Sergeant Mace again, you see! Get me old uniform on! Be polishing buttons again soon!"

Then he looked at his hands with their crippled fingers.

"Ah—labour corps for me this time. Cleanin' out the bleedin' latrines." And he went back into the kitchen, somewhat punctured and a little less exultant.

"Well," said the Bo'sn, rolling a cigarette and running his tongue along the gummed strip. "I've had my go, I reckon. Some of you young bastards can have a basinful now. See how you like it. I've been through it. Now it's your turn."

"It's everybody's turn," I said.

"Damned good job too!"

"I don't want no war," said Tom, studying his

matchstick. " What I want to know is," he continued, pointing his matchstick across the table to emphasize his point, "why don't they send a lord over there? What's the good of Chamberlain goin' over there? Hitler won't listen to him. Ain't they got any lords to send? "

" I'm afraid Hitler wouldn't be very impressed with them as a bunch, Tom."

" Well, it don't matter," said Sandy, the second engineer. " It don't matter." He got up from the table and knotted his sweat cloth around his neck. " What I says is, you've got to die sometime. We've all got to die. I'm not afraid of dyin'. Bloody excitin', I think, to die. You'll know then. You'll know what hundreds of people 'ud give a fortune to know—what's on the other side. We'll all find out sometime!" He disappeared up the companion ladder.

But chiefly, I think, it was a rather pleasant kind of excitement that they felt whenever they thought about the prospect, which was not very often or very much in any case. To those who listened to the radio bulletins on the bridge the football news was of equal importance to the foreign news, and sometimes of greater importance. It was usually retailed first in the deckies' mess and provoked the greater discussion. The rest of the news came as an afterthought.

" Arsenal won, one—nil, with five minutes extra time. Got the goal in the extra time. Must have been a bloody fine game. Like to have seen it! And the Czechs have mobilized and Chamberlain's come home without seeing Hitler again. One—nil, bloody good game it must have been too! "

And often, when the hour for the news bulletin approached, I would say, with affected unconcern :

"What about some news, Sparks?"

"Oh, bloody 'ell! I'd forgotten all about it," Sparks would say, lifting his head and turning on into the little cabin and bridge-house the grave and measured accents that seemed to proclaim the black-out of all life.

Mostly, however, there was a sense of excitement. It was slightly stimulating. All ships bound for Bear Island and the White Sea had received instructions on passage north to alter course and make for Iceland instead. Should we be able to return to Grimsby or should we be ordered to Fleetwood? If the Admiralty took over the *Lincoln Star*, as they almost certainly would, what chances did each of them stand of being kept on? All these points were debated across the tea table, with knives and forks emphasizing arguments, while I sat there listening, feeling a thousand miles from home and very lonely.

For myself my chief longing was to get back, to get home among the people and sights and sounds that I knew. I felt suddenly that it was desperately urgent that I should be there. I wanted to know what my own world was doing about it all in order that I might do it too. I felt for the first time, quite suddenly, that I was not one of these men. It was a feeling that came entirely from within myself. They did nothing to make me feel that way but I knew that their whole reaction, their whole way of thinking and behaving about this, was quite different from mine. In many ways, I saw with shame, it was a good deal better and finer, but it was different. And I could communicate my thoughts to none of them. Their thoughts and feelings about what seemed to be approaching were for the most part so personal to themselves and seemed to me, in that time of strain, to embrace so narrow a horizon that, as I sat listening to them, I wanted to shout and yell and smash something and scream at them about the destruction of hope, the death of youth and love, the disappearance of beauty from the world, the swallowing up in universal night of everything that makes it worth while to live upon this sweet earth. But I knew it would have been of no use. So I said instead, "Yes, I suppose we'll probably have to go back to Fleetwood," and "Yes, I expect the Admiralty will take the ship over and make her into a minesweeper." I told the Chief Engineer, who was in the Reserve, that he'd be in the navy again soon now.

At last this feeling and the ache to get home got the better of me. We had been circling slowly round upon the banks off the North Cape for a week catching very little but "soldiers" and small "sprags," young cod. Sometimes the jagged outline of North Cape stood clear and hard against a blue sky. At others it was draped with cloud or hidden altogether by fog or drizzling rain. They shot the trawl and brought it in and shot it again. The catches were always poor. They gutted, washed and stowed the fish and swore because there was so little of it. And as they did these things the toothed mountain of the North Cape lay now ahead and now astern, now to port and now to starboard. The *Lincoln Star* moved slowly round and round, rocking upon the swell, and other ships kept her company, rocking too. The voices in Sparks' cabin told me daily what was happening in the outer world while I circled round and round.

" I want to get home, Skipper," I said at last.

The Skipper had seldom left the bridge during the whole of that week. He seemed hardly ever to eat. Sometimes Jack Johnson brought up a bowl of soup, sometimes a plate of sandwiches. The Skipper did not often finish either. " I never eat much while I'm fishing," he said. And he scarcely ever slept except for brief half-hours snatched now and then when he lay down on the settee in the chart-room. Round his chin now there was quite a fine red beard. All of us had beards more or less but I rather less than more since I shaved mine off every few days, partly to give myself something to do and partly to enjoy the groomed and tailored feeling it gave when I shut my eyes and ran my fingers over my face.

" You want to get home? " said the Skipper in astonishment. " What for? "

" Well, I don't know," I said, unable to explain what I felt. " Don't you want to get home? "

" No fear I don't. Not till I've got my catch."

" What about the missus? "

" Oh, she'll be all right! "

But that evening he said:

" Had a wire from the missus this evening. Gettin' a bit anxious it seems."

" Yes, I expect she is."

" Can't go home till I've got my catch though."

" Well, I hope to God you get some bloody fish soon,"

I burst out. "I want to get back!... I must get home."

It was the evening of Tuesday, September 27th, 1938. The *Lincoln Star* moved slowly, rocking a little, over a sea of ink. The clear night sky was filled with stars spread like a bright dome above us. The moon above the dark mountains made a pathway upon the water. High up and far away inland it shone with a faint sheen upon old snow. I went out upon the bridge-deck to be alone. I could not any longer listen to the Skipper humming snatches of jazz, or to the voices that came over the radio proclaiming war and the day's catch in one breath, or to the Bo'sn's pleasant anticipations of what was in store for "you young bastards." It was silent out here, thank God, except for the gentle lap of water along the hull and the creak and strain of the trawling wires. A cool sweet puff of air blew sometimes out of nowhere, utterly odourless and pure, and died away again, making the spanker sail flap a little upon its boom. The entrance to the deckies' fo'c'sle glowed dimly in the dark bulk of the bows and from the stove-pipe for'ard a spark fled and vanished now and then upon the night. They were sleeping down there before the trawl came in.

Suddenly overhead, lower than the stars and yet among them, the awful veils and draperies of the Northern Lights drew together out of heaven, shifted and changed and drew asunder until the firmament moved with their unearthly brilliance. The curtain was going up.

"Good God!" I said. "It's impossible. It won't happen."

CHAPTER XII

We spent a week circling slowly and patiently round and round within sight of North Cape, one of a little company of tireless ships. Sometimes this slowly manoeuvring fleet separated a bit so that its members lay dotted far apart about the great disc of the sea, some far away and hull down upon the horizon, but at other times they drew together and passed so close to one another that more than once I thought they would collide. One day, when a thick fog blotted out the world and we moved through a solid grey wall hooting dismally, a cluster of faint lights grew suddenly together out of nothing right before us. As the other trawler passed us like a ghost ship only a few yards away upon our port bow a voice yelled through a megaphone, " Ain't you got no bleedin' whistle? "

" Well, I'm damned! " said the Skipper. For the whistle had blown with nerve-shattering effect every quarter of an hour day and night for the last twenty-four hours.

" It's nerves," said Tom at the wheel. " Got the wind up, that's what he's got."

But in all that time we caught no fish. A few young cod and haddock, some small coal-fish and a multitude of " soldiers." But no real fish, they said. They shovelled back into the sea more than they stowed away, leaving astern a trail of corpses over which the Kittiwakes screamed and swooped and fought.

North Cape. One of a little company of tireless ships.

The men grumbled quite a bit about this. What was the good of sticking around here? Anyone could see there was no fish here. He ought to go farther in and do a bit of poaching under the coast. He ought to go farther out along the edge and try for some of the bigger fish. He ought to go round the east side, that was where they were doing best, so Sparks said. He ought to try round Grimsey Island.

"We'll never get home at this rate."

"I'd be surprised if we made seven hundred pounds this trip the way he's goin' on."

"Trouble with him is 'e don't know the grounds. I could a' told 'im he wouldn't find no fish round here."

"What we want's a man as'll take a chance now and then, like 'Smiler' Wraite. He's the lad. He don't care where he gets 'is fish so long as he gets 'em."

And it seemed to them that fortune had singled out the *Lincoln Star* and her crew as a target for the most outrageous of her slings and arrows.

"Well, I dunno. They're doin' all right at Langanes," said Sparks. "*Kingston Pearl* took a hundred baskets there last haul."

"We'll never get home."

"There's a Jonah aboard this blasted ship!"

"Hell!" said the Skipper. "We'll steam eastward a bit."

Next time the trawl came in they did not shoot it again but stowed it along the scuppers and, with the otter boards slung at her gallows, the *Lincoln Star* turned eastwards. The North Cape fell away and diminished beneath the western horizon.

It was a grey colourless day when we arrived within sight of Langanes again. We could see the breakers leaping in tongues of white about the dark feet of the cliffs. A low even pall of cloud covered all the sky like a blanket but over the distant mountains there were bars and shafts of light that lit their lower slopes while their tops were hidden. They shot the trawl again in ninety-five fathoms and, for the hundredth time but with new hope, they watched it sink away into the darkness.

"Hope to God we get something here," said the Skipper. "I had another wire from the missus this morning. She's in the hell of a state. But I can't go home till I've got my catch. I just can't. Away she goes!"

The *Lincoln Star* leapt forward once again round to starboard, tracing upon the grey sea a curve of troubled water at her stern. The bow wave broke frothing on each side of her and she trembled with the pulse of her engines. They were like a heart pumping new blood through her and the ship too seemed filled with a new hope. The wires rattled outwards from the winches and the rope pads upon them, marking off the twenty fathom lengths, followed one another in the same steady procession, up, over the pulley blocks, down into the water.

"All out!"

The engine telegraph rang "slow." The bow wave diminished and the *Lincoln Star* settled down once again to her slow patient circling, towing her straining wires, under the shadow of Langanes, a low flat finger pointing east. Far away to westward a smudge of smoke showed where another trawler was circling slowly too.

"And again, men. All together! Heave-hup!"

We dug our S-shaped hooks into the mass of netting that hung like the inert corpse of some gigantic sea beast, cold and wet and dead, over the starboard rail. We leant back on our hooks together and a foot or so of net came in.

"And again, men. Hup!"

Presently we had brought in enough of the net to get a rope strop round the waist of the narrower part of the trawl that still hung overboard. Then we stopped digging with our hooks and stood in a row gazing over the rail at a point on the surface of the water about twenty feet from the ship's side. It was the most important and crucial spot on the whole extent of the globe that we were looking at in that moment. More important for our little world than either Godesberg or Munich. What we saw there made us turn to one another smiling and saying, "That's better, anyhow!" For in the middle of the oily dome of water welling up from below there rose slowly and majestically the snout of the cod-end. It was not lean and thin like the muzzle of a hungry dog but round and swollen like a huge dark breast. It came heavily and ponderously to the surface in the middle of its aura of bubbles. We could see great curved gleaming flanks and bellies trapped within it. Mouths and eyes gaped through the meshes. "At last," they said, "We've got some fish."

"Jilson!"

The bag of the cod-end swung up out of the water and swayed above the fore-deck, dripping, vast and pregnant, a huge womb swollen with multitudinous life. When the Bo'sn, stooping beneath it among the pattering drops that rained off it, untied the slip-knot it suddenly collapsed and spewed forth its innards over the deck, a slithering torrent of monsters that flapped and wriggled and lay still, gaping. It was as though death came upon every one of them in an instant of grotesque amazement.

There was something about them that was not entirely fish-like as they lay there on the deck in a heap. Occasional twitches and flutters ran through the heap. When one of them gave a spasmodic jump or flap its neighbour immediately answered so that little epidemics of feeble ineffectual movement ran through the company of them from time to time, faded away and left them all gasping and exhausted. Soon they were corpses stiffening into death. They were caricaturishly human. Had I not beheld those gaping mouths elsewhere, not marked before those goggling hopeless eyes? They were glazing now into a stare of uncomprehending stupidity as though death were not affording any satisfactory explanation of all those things which are so perplexing for cod-fish during life. Some of the mouths opened a little wider as though about to speak. But the words were never uttered and it seemed as though death rushed in and stifled them. And in a minute or so they were just a high, cold, wet mountain of things, a mound of lifelessness. Something goes out even from a fish at death and leaves a quite impersonal husk.

But what splendid husks they were, magnificent in death! There were hundreds of mottled green cod-fish, many of them three or four feet in length, each with the barbel on his chin like a tiny goatee beard. There were as many haddock, much smaller, silver with a dark streak along each side. There were coal-fish or saithe, even larger than the true cod, silver below and black above. There were dark grey or mottled brown cat-fish with their bull-dog jaws and backwardly curved teeth, a continuous fin running the whole length of their back, a monstrous horrifying beast. It was a joke to pick the cat-fish up and make them hang on to the trawling wires by their teeth. You had to be careful to grasp them behind the back of the head when you played this joke because if a finger got in the way of those powerful snapping jaws the joke was not so funny. There were plaice too, flat and mottled dark brown above and white beneath, and there were delicate soles like leaves. And slimy skates with lugubrious expressions and a few dog-fish like little sharks with slit-like venomous eyes and rough skins. There were other things too, the trash and rubbish grubbed up from the sea bottom by the all-engulfing trawl, large broken urchins and dead-men's fingers and great star-fish with many arms like suns that bent and straightened infinitely slowly and painfully as they lay on the deck.

"Ah!" said the Skipper, wading about among all this nearly knee deep. "This is something like. There's fine fish for you! Fine fish here! That's champion fish that is! We'll do all right if we go on like this. Put a buoy over, Jim."

So they put the dan buoy out to mark the spot and shot the trawl again.

On the great fishing grounds of northern Europe, the White Sea, Bear Island and Iceland live all these bottom-living fish that are caught with the trawl, the cod, the hake, the haddock, the plaice, the sole and several others. And through the waters above the " banks " the herring and the mackerel swim in shoals. On the " edge " live the ling and the halibut, caught with the trawl and with the line. There are many kinds of fish too that you may not have heard of but which are caught upon the northern banks and find their way to you as just " fish." There is the coal-fish or saithe, which is a kind of cod and is often sold as such, and the cat-fish with his bull-dog jaw and speckled skin. Both of these are good to eat and you would hardly know the difference. The English know very little about food anyway and to the working folk who buy them fish is just fish. It all looks much the same fried in batter and eaten on a piece of newspaper with salt and pepper.

The fish population of the northern seas differs greatly from area to area and even from bank to bank but the differences are those of proportion usually rather than differences in the actual kinds of fish that the trawlers expect to catch. On the Newfoundland banks, along the coast of Norway to the White Sea and around Iceland the cod is by far the most abundant of all fish, but others also occur, especially the haddock, the plaice and the herring. But as you go southward into warmer waters the cod

Cod-end.

becomes less plentiful. In the North Sea the haddock and the plaice are more important than the cod. Farther south still towards the Bay of Biscay the hake and the pollack are the main fish the trawlers catch. Here, in the southern waters of the great European fishing ground, the cod, though still taken, is comparatively scarce and unimportant.

The make-up of the catch the trawlers may expect in any area, the kinds of fish that live upon the banks, their size and their condition, depend on many things. The temperature of the water is one of the chief of these, for all marine creatures live within a range of temperature which is most suitable to them. The time of year is important because all fish do not spawn at quite the same time. The depth of the water is important too, because the various kinds of fish spawn and live at different levels. Again, the condition of the sea-floor counts also, for on this depends the abundance or scarcity of the food upon which each kind of fish prefers to feed. The cod, for instance, loves a " hard bottom," as the fishermen say, of stones, but the haddock prefers a " soft bottom " of mud and sand. The plaice also loves sandy shallows. Finally, there is the strength and direction of the currents over the banks since the eggs of all bottom-living fish are, with the ruthless improvidence of nature, shed into the sea. They, and the tiny developing fish that hatch from them, drift at God's mercy whithersoever the currents and the tides may take them.

In the very early spring, about February or March, the cod and haddock spawn upon the banks to the south and east of Iceland. The cod sheds her eggs in water between twenty and forty fathoms deep but the haddock chooses rather deeper water. The eggs of both are clear crystal spheres which float aimlessly at the mercy of waves and currents. They drift clockwise around the coast with the revolving current that encircles the island. As they go they are devoured by teeming enemies, the floating population of the sea that drifts with them. And the little fish that hatch from them are born into a world full of hazards in which millions of them perish.

The prodigality and waste of nature are amazing. The majority of sea fish, certainly all food fish, take no interest whatever in their eggs after they have shed them, or in the tiny frail creatures that hatch from them. The defenceless drifting infants are exposed to every risk conceivable. They are devoured by hosts of enemies. They drift into waters unsuitable for their growth. They are washed ashore and wither away, drying up like seed fallen upon stony ground. In fact the odds against every egg winning through and finally becoming a cod-fish are enormous. As a compensation for this the cod, and nearly all sea fishes, sheds millions of eggs at a time. Most animals that exercise no care for their young but leave them to the tender mercies of nature breed so profusely that by sheer numbers, by mere prodigality and ruthless expenditure of young life, they maintain the race. So the cod-fish sheds five million eggs at a time. Some fish shed even more. If every egg shed by every fish were able to develop and become a cod each year it would only take a few years to fill the seas of all the world so packed tight with cod-fish that there would be no room for any more. But this disaster will never happen to us whatever others may befall since innumerable dangers, thank heaven, surround the egg before it hatches. They do not diminish when it has hatched and become a minute transparent fry. When at last it has won through them and has settled upon the bottom as a grown cod-fish mankind adds himself to the number of its enemies, sweeping the cod-fish in millions yearly from the banks.

The eggs are shed into the upper layers of the sea in water between twenty and forty fathoms deep. Presently the egg hatches and becomes a tiny glassy fry only a few centimetres long, all head and eyes, curled upon the diminishing yolk of its egg. The eggs of fishes have yolk, food substance stored within themselves, just as have nearly all other eggs, whether of fishes, birds, reptiles or mammals. The nutritive yolk hangs as a sac beneath the young fish embryo which feeds on it until it has presently disappeared. The little fish grows longer and becomes mottled with dark spots. Soon it begins to feed for itself, after the yolk has all been used up, on the green plant-slime and on the clouds of tiny floating creatures that fill the sea around it. When it is about an inch long the young cod, or the young haddock, and the young of other kinds of fish as well, adopt a really astonishing method of protecting themselves from the millions of foes that surround them, drifting where they drift and filling the seas with voracious life. They seek the shelter of those giant jelly-fish, the "sluthers," which float in hosts in all the waters above the banks, trailing their long stinging tentacles and pulsing like great disembodied hearts. Beneath these protecting bells the little fish live in clouds, darting actively in and out, but keeping always within their shadow. There, guarded by the stinging armament of their friendly foster parent, they are for the most part out of reach of their enemies. It is strange that they are never themselves caught in the deadly mesh of those tentacles but in some way, which is not understood, the jelly-fish tolerate them and seem able to distinguish between them and the other creatures that come within their range. Later, when they are little, glassy, almost perfect fish about an inch and a half to two inches long, the young cod or haddock begin to leave the upper layers of the sea, forsaking their hospitable jelly-fish. At the same time they begin to spread out into the bays and estuaries along the coast and into the deeper waters of the banks. About May or June around Iceland they reach the bottom, change their diet and begin to feed upon the things that crawl and wriggle and creep among the stones. And there they stay until the trawl, like a submarine cataclysm, sweeps them up in a fearful cloud of sand with all their brothers, crushing down the friendly forests in which they live.

By the time the young cod have settled upon the bottom they have come far with the current from the southern banks where the eggs were shed. By the autumn they are round the northern side of the island. But when the spring comes again the grown fish migrate southwards, back to the banks on the southern side, making the complete circle of the coast. Here the last spring's young cod, in their turn, spurt into the unregarding sea their five million crystal globes. Through the drift of the young northwards with the current, and the migration of the young fish south to spawn, they encircle the island clockwise every year. The fishermen go to the south of the island in the early part of the year when the big fish come to spawn upon the southern banks. Later in the year they go north and east, round the North Cape and round Langanes. The trawlermen know by experience where and when to find the best fish. In the autumn round the north coast, where the *Lincoln Star* swept slowly day and night, and fish were mostly small yearling cod and haddock hatched the previous spring. But on the edge of the northern banks were bigger fish which seek deeper water than the younger ones. Fishermen have a fish lore of their own and will tell you a great deal about the fish they catch without bothering much about the explanation of what they know. They say that in the winter the fishing is best in the daytime but that in the summer it is best at night. I do not know why this is and Jim was not worrying why it was. He just told me that. If I didn't like it I could leave it. But in the summer, they say, the fish leave the bottom when the sunshine is bright and come up towards the surface so that in the daytime they tend to avoid the trawl. Fishermen say, too, that when the "sluthers" are numerous the fishing is poor and an abundance of these great inert things is a sign of a poor ground. But this is not so hard to explain since the "sluthers", perhaps, devour the floating young stages of the innumerable bottom-living creatures the fish feed upon. Any ground where the waters are heavily infested with jelly-fish during the spring will, later in the year, be poor in food for fish. And always the trawlermen say that the best fish are to be found within the three-mile territorial limit where the fishing is forbidden and protected by prowling Danish gun-boats. But that, of course, is only to be expected.

All the bottom-living fish start life as drifting fry and surface-living young as do the cod and haddock. They spawn in the spring in the waters over the banks, shedding their millions of eggs in the upper layers and leaving them to drift as they grow up until, in the summer, they sink down to the bottom and begin to feed on the teeming creatures that live there. The flat-fish, such as the plaice, the sole, the turbot and the halibut, do not acquire their flattened shape and one-sided colouring until they sink. Up to that time they are tiny symmetrical fish like the young cod. But when they sink down they lie upon their sides and flatten out. The plaice, the sole and the halibut lie on their left sides. The turbot lies upon his right side. Then the lower eye, since it would be of no use buried in the sand, travels round to the upper side of the head, taking its blood vessels and nerves with it, and there from a position on the side of the head alongside its fellow, it directs its proud unwinking stare upwards. Both eyes, elevated upon knobs so that the fish can bury itself almost entirely save for its eyes, stand together on the same side of the head and the fish swims always on one side.

But all fish do not spawn at quite the same time even

They lay still, gaping.

on the same banks, nor do they all spawn at the same level. The cod, for instance, spawns upon the Iceland banks mainly in February or March. But on the Newfoundland banks, where the water is much colder, it does not spawn until July. The cod, again, spawns in water where the depth is between twenty and forty fathoms, the haddock prefers deeper water and the coal-fish spawns upon the "edge" in deeper water still. These three, the cod, the haddock and the coal-fish, all belonging to the cod family, are the most common fish around Iceland and fill the trawls almost to the exclusion of all the others. But there are also plaice, a few soles, cat-fish and some turbot. Now and then, in deep water, a great halibut, a lop-sided giant, is taken. But in the waters above the banks there are shoals of herring which the Icelanders catch with small motor drifters and with seine nets.

The herring is different in its manner of life from all the commoner northern food fishes except the mackerel. Instead of living on the bottom it swims in shoals in the upper layers feeding upon the drifting clouds of red shrimp-like creatures that abound in the seas around the northern coasts during the summer. The herring lays sticky eggs in clusters among the stones upon the bottom in shallow water near the coast. All down our coasts the herring comes inshore in swarms to spawn and lay its eggs. It is then that the herring season starts and the little drifters lie in wait at night with their hanging miles of net. The spawning of the herring brings a livelihood to thousands of hard working, brave and cheerful people from John o'Groats to Land's End. It comes in June to the Shetlanders and the people of Aberdeen. To Grimsby, Hull and Newcastle it comes in July, and in October to Yarmouth and Lowestoft. But in the south, round the coasts of Devon and Cornwall, the herring does not spawn until about January. This is not a movement southwards of the herring shoals but a successively later and later movement inwards of the shoals towards the coast and the shallow waters. Yearly the fisher girls follow it south, bringing to southern towns the loud ring of their Scottish laughter and the morning tramp of feet.

But in the North Sea, the Norwegian Sea, around Iceland, the White Sea, Spitzbergen and Bear Island, the trawlers from Britain, from France, from Germany, Holland, Denmark and Norway are at work at all times of the year and in all weathers. The fishing is best in the spring when the big fish move to the spawning banks. It is poorest in the autumn. It is hardest for the fishermen in the winter when the ropes and gear freeze stiff and are caked with solid ice, when there is fog for days at a time, when gales constantly force the ships to run for shelter in the fjords and bays of a forbidding coast. Dangers and hazards are familiar to fishermen. Not even Death himself is quite a stranger. Nearly every man in the *Lincoln Star* had been wrecked at some time or other upon the coast of Iceland or Bear Island or in the White Sea. The Skipper had been pulled overboard with the trawl the previous winter and had been hauled out unconscious after twenty minutes almost lost in the icy darkness, weighed down by sea-boots and oilskins.

Jim had broken a rib only three months ago when a sea threw him against the casing. Sambo had been taken off a wreck on the coast of Bear Island whither his ship had driven in a blinding snow squall. Tom had run ashore on Langanes in a thick fog. The Sergeant had been twenty-seven hours in an open boat in Faxa Bay during a winter gale, losing his fingers through frost-bite. Thus dangerously do men live in this year of Our Lord and earn the bread they eat. Thus arduously they gather in the harvest of the sea.

CHAPTER XIII

WHEN the trawl had spilt upon the deck its slithering, slippery mound of fish they got the net over and away again as soon as possible. And then they began what is, perhaps, the most important part of the fisherman's job, gutting the fish. Down in the deckies' mess-room there was a large printed notice which perpetually reminded them how important it is. It is essential, the notice said, to remove all traces of guts and blood from the body cavity and to see that each fish is thoroughly washed inside before it is stowed in the fish-room. For on the care which is taken with this process depends the condition of the fish when it arrives in port and therefore the price which it will fetch in the market.

Realizing this, and remembering the owner's injunction to keep out of the way, I did not offer my invaluable services in the pound but usually sat on a bollard nearby watching. It was good to see their swift tough hands ripping open white or silver bellies with one slick stroke of the knife and to listen to their fragmentary talk as they worked. Each man took up a position in the pound and dealt with the fish within arm's reach. They only gutted fish of a marketable size but exactly what the limits of that size were I never quite found out. They must be laid down, of course, but it seemed to me to be largely a matter of individual judgment for some seemed to reject larger fish than others. In general, however, they all selected or rejected fish of approximately the same size. And when the gutting was finished Jim and the Bo'sn would pick over the heap of rejected fish that remained, turning them over with their boots or with their hands, sometimes selecting and gutting one that appeared to them to be too good a fish to waste. I was, in fact, astonished at the waste which trawling involves. When the gutting was finished hundreds of small cod and haddock and still more small plaice and little delicate soles lay dead and unused upon the deck and were swept back into the sea to feed the screaming birds. Each one of these, returning as carrion to its own waters, was the potential producer of millions of eggs next spring, hundreds of new fish next summer. And this, indeed, is one of the problems of the trawling grounds, for the trawl is a ruthlessly efficient instrument. It sweeps up regardless everything that comes into its gaping mouth. It not only scours the ground clean of fish of every sort and size but tears up also the molluscs, the worms, the crustacea and all the life of the sea bottom on which the fish feed. Scores of trawls comb the grounds every day of every month of the year without respite wherever food fishes are to be found. They are ruining the grounds not only for themselves but for the longshoremen, the seine netters and line fishermen who also make their living by the same harvest. To avoid this waste as much as possible the trawls are made with a mesh of such a size that small fish and other animals escape through them, but once a fair quantity of fish are packed in the cod-end they form a solid mass that blocks the meshes far up the net, and so the trawl scoops up every living thing that lies within its path. The great steel bobbins on the foot-rope churn up the bottom, smashing and battering down the fronded undergrowths and lightly rooted branches that give shelter, the stones and rocks that provide a foothold, the sand and mud that make an oozy world for beasts to live in.

So, when the trawl had vomited all this out upon the deck and the good fish had been picked out and gutted, hundreds of others that looked good enough to me still remained. The Sergeant came for'ard and tipped his cook's cap on the back on his head. He picked out a slimy skate or two, a few plaice. " Ah, nice bit o' fish to-night," he said and carried his booty away. But the rest lay there dead and drying on the deck, waiting for the hose and broom that would sweep them back into the sea, cut off by the thousand in their prime.

The men in the gutting pound bent over their work, saying very little, laughing from time to time. They took each victim by the gill cover with the left hand and turned it on its back. Holding it thus with its head up but its tail on the deck they ripped open its belly with a clean swift cut of a sharp knife from the chin to the anus. If you listened carefully each cut made a soft, hollow, labial sound. Then they tore out the guts with the forefinger and thumb of the right hand from before backwards, using the knife fore and aft to detach the long clammy pale pink tube as far forward and as far back as possible. Then the body cavity was empty except for the flaccid yellow liver. That was cut out and thrown into a basket.

Gutting.

They used gloves for this job for you cannot gut several hundreds of fish a day without getting sore, torn fingers.

I have been trying to recapture the smell of fish that became now part of our daily lives. It is an alkaline, soapy but a clean, rather sweet smell. Only in a crowded, warm and narrow space such as the saloon where we ate did I occasionally wish that some other smell could have been invented for fish. Out on the deck it was a healthy, marine, animal aroma, pungent and honest like sweat. But it clung about us all like a presence. When I myself was in it and among the men who carried it about with them I noticed it very little, but when I came down to the saloon after an hour on the bridge it seemed to be a tangible thing that sat with us at table for the men brought the smell down with them on their boots and on their clothes.

But there are other aromas, other essences, which float around a trawler when at work. Some of the most remarkable and significant issued from the little housing on the main deck right over the stern where there were pressure boilers for boiling down the liver. Sparks had charge of them and he spent a lot of time attending to his charges when we were on the fishing grounds. The savour that arose as a result of his ministrations was hot, sweet and oily, a little sickening, and it was accompanied by clouds of steam which at times streamed out of the boiler house and fled over the stern upon the wind. But to me it was not unfamiliar for it reminded me of the meaty whaling station smells I had once been used to. But everyone else in the ship affected various degrees of disgust and went past the door, whenever Sparks was busy inside, holding their noses and making unprintable allusions.

When enough baskets filled with disembodied livers had accumulated for'ard Jack Johnson carried them along the deck to the boiler-house aft.

" Hi, Sparks! . . . Livers! "

" Oh, bloody 'ell! What—again? "

And Sparks would come running out of his cabin on the bridge and tip the quivering masses out of the baskets into the boilers, clamp down the tops and turn on the steam. That was all you had to do. You had to keep the steam pressure up and in a few hours, but I forget how many, the clear cod-liver oil was run off at the bottom of the boilers and stored in barrels. Part of the proceeds of the sale of the cod-liver oil went to each man on board as part of his share in the trip. But why these duties fell to the wireless operator I do not know. However, Sparks imparted a certain dignity to this simple but important office and referred always to " my livers," " my boilers " and " my steam pressure." "I must go and see how my pressure's getting on." " I must attend to my livers." Exactly thus did the Sergeant refer to " my galley " and Jim to " my fish-room." Exactly thus did the Skipper say " my ship."

The men did not talk much while they worked in the gutting pound. There was too much to do. When they did talk they never paused in their work or looked up from it but spoke always stooping over the fish they held so that their voices were often lost in their chests. Only Billie sometimes threw back his head and laughed and usually it was the Bo'sn's voice that one heard above the others. Jim gave an order from time to time.

Each fish, when it had been gutted, was thrown across the deck to the pound on the port side. They threw the smaller ones with a sideways fling of the arm without straightening from their stooping posture and without looking where they threw them. But the larger fish they threw heavily with both arms, grunting. As they worked the eviscerated fish somersaulted continually through the air in gleaming arcs from the starboard to the port side. They landed with a series of heavy, hollow plops. The heap of gashed and opened corpses on one side grew while the lifeless mountain dropped by the trawl on the starboard side as steadily diminished. Round the feet of the stooping figures spread a slippery shambles of blood and slime and collapsed pale pink tubes.

"Know old Tolly as worked as deckie in the *Ocean Gem*?"

"Aye. I remember 'im. Square-'ead, that's what 'e is."

"He ain't a bleedin' square-'ead. 'E's a bleedin' Russian."

Over she goes! A silver haddock gleaming in an arc from starboard to port.

"'Ow d'you know? What's the difference anyway?"

"I seen a letter 'e wrote."

"What lingo was it in?"

Another coming over!

"No lingo I ever saw before. But I bet it wasn't Dutch, anyway!"

"Go on! You don't know the bloody difference, you don't."

As they talked their gloved hands never stopped. They reached out among the mound of fish around their feet, cut, tore out, and flung the corpses over, reaching out for the next in the same movement.

I envied them for having something to do, something to occupy their minds and their hands while I sat brooding upon a bollard nearby wondering how many more such hauls as this we should have to get before we brought the trawl in for the last time and finally turned homeward.

It took perhaps an hour or so to gut all the fish that were worth keeping from that haul. At the end of that time the mound of corpses lay on the port instead of on the starboard side and the belly of every corpse of which it was composed was empty, flat and collapsed. But the eyes still gaped and the eyes still goggled with the same stare of silly astonishment. They turned the hoses on and filled up the port pound with sea water that ran frothing away over the deck. Then the men stood among the gutted fish in the pound and kneaded them with their feet in the swirling water, washing all the blood away from the fish so as to leave the empty bodies clean and sweet, each one just a cylinder of muscle. They were ready to be stowed below. Jim and the Bo'sn went over them picking one up here and there to make sure that it was clean inside.

"Right!" said Jim finally. "Get the covers off!"

"You ought to come down to the fish-room and give us a hand stowing the fish," said Sambo as they

The washing pound.

lifted the covers from the hatches. " You ought really."

" I might be in the way. The owners told me particularly not to get in the way so perhaps I'd better not."

" When the owners work aboard here," said Sambo with emphasis, prodding me in the chest with his forefinger, " they can talk about gettin' in the road. You come along down. If you want to, that is."

So, when the covers had been removed, I climbed down the iron ladder into the chill catacombs below.

Each of the four compartments of the fish-room was traversed by a central alleyway flanked by deep shelves. These were themselves divided at regular intervals by vertical partitions. The foremost compartment was partly blocked by a white cliff of powdered ice, taken aboard before we left Grimsby. Sambo attacked it with a shovel, loosening at its foot a heap of ice which he spread upon the shelves. Sambo always sang directly he felt a shovel in his hand and the chill gloom of the fish-room rang immediately with his tenor voice charged with enough pathos to awaken all the fish. " I love yew. Yes—I dew. I l-o-o-ve yew."

" Bleedin' awful row," said Tom, descending the steel ladder. " Make all the fish sit up, I shouldn't wonder."

The fish taken in earlier hauls were lying on the shelves graded according to size, all the cod of one size on one shelf and all those of another size on another shelf. All the cod were stowed in one compartment of the fish-room, the large ones lying packed neatly head to tail like giant sardines in a tin, the smaller ones lying irregularly, bedded down in layers of ice. In another compartment were all the haddock, and in another all the coal-fish, similarly neatly graded and stowed. But since the trip had not been very successful until now many of the shelves were empty. One had a single occupant only, a great clammy flattened mound of fish flesh lying in its own bed of ice. It was a huge halibut taken a day or so ago. I was led to it reverently by the arm. We stood gazing at it in a slightly awestruck but appreciative silence, as though taking a last view of a royal body lying in state. I thought perhaps I ought to take off my cap.

" Aye. It's a beauty, is that," said Jim. " 'Tisn't often you get a fish that size in the trawl."

The fish-room was Jim's especial province. It was his job to see that the fish were properly stowed and packed down in ice. He had to see that the temperature of the fish-room remained constant and did not rise much above freezing. It was his business to see that no fish was stowed unless it had been properly gutted and washed so that it was sweet and clean inside. " My fish." " My fish-room." He looked around his fish-room with pride and conducted me from shelf to shelf by the arm, stooping beneath the doorways and the overhead pipes of the refrigerating plant. It was an impressive sight, this great mausoleum of fish so neatly and trimly laid upon their shelves.

" Well, I do my best, like. Can't do more," said Jim. " We'll finish up this shelf with big 'uns here, see? Then we'll start a new shelf for the big 'uns. This lot here can do with some more small sprags from what I can see of it. There's still plenty of room there. We can start a new shelf for the coalies. . . ."

On deck the fish were piled into baskets and each basket, when it was full, was lowered by Jack Johnson down the hatchway to Jim and Tom who stood below, arms raised to take it. These baskets were used as a rough measure of the catch. As each one was filled and lowered down the hatchway into the fish-room the Bo'sn tallied it. When all the fish had gone below he called up to the bridge, cupping his hands about his mouth, " Forty-four sprag, twenty-three 'docks, fifteen coalies, eight plaice—ninety baskets, Skipper! "

" Good-oh! " said the Skipper, rubbing his hands together. " We'll keep our mouths shut about this! "

When the fish from each basket had been taken out and arranged according to size upon the shelves the empty basket was handed up again through the hatchway.

" Comin' up, Basher! "

And another full one came down in its place.

" Got 'im. Right—let go, Basher! "

The fish already lying there were cold and stiff and hard like wood but those newly gutted and washed were limp and soft. The larger ones you grasped around the body just in front of the tail with one hand and by the gill cover with the other. You swung them thus as far back down the shelves as you could. That was a long way when Jim or Tom did it but not so far when I did it. And when the fish had to be stowed at the back of the shelves Jim and Tom lay full length upon the cold bodies of those already there snug in their bed of ice, grunting as they packed the new-comers in place. They took the fish as they were handed to them and arranged them neatly head to tail from the back of the shelf outwards. When each shelf was full Sambo spread shovelfuls of ice over the cold corpses much as earth is shovelled upon a grave.

The after compartment of the fish-room was as yet empty. This was the compartment in which coal had been stowed on passage north and where Billie and Sambo had laboured every watch, shovelling the coal through the tunnel into the stokehold. There was no trace of coal there now. It had been thoroughly hosed down and the shelves, made of scrubbed wooden boards that ran into slots in the vertical partitions, were waiting empty and ready for the fish they were to hold.

" Well," said Jim, hands on hips, " Maybe we'll be able to start on the after-compartment if we keep on getting hauls like this."

Nothing I found, could be chillier and less responsive to the touch than dead fish. The fingers very soon became numbed from handling them. I wanted to stop sometimes and beat my hands against my sides to warm them but none of the others seemed to feel any need to do so for their hands were tough and hard. Jim and Tom, crawling about over the bodies of the fish upon the shelves, grunting as they fitted the icy slabs of flesh in place, never stopped for a second. As soon as I had heaved one fish to them and stood panting awhile I found they were ready for another. And as soon as each basket was finished there was

Jack Johnson in the square of sky above staring down balefully over another one.

But presently he said, " Only flats now—sprags and 'docks is finished," and handed down a basket of plaice and soles looking like fleshy shiny leaves. They put them all on another shelf and Sambo packed them down with ice.

" That's the lot," said Jack Johnson above. We heard the Bo'sn shouting up to the bridge. " Ninety baskets, Skipper! "

" Good-oh! "

I was sweating hot in the chill air of the fish-room though my fingers were numb. I was warm inside too with a righteous glow. I had been lending a hand—of sorts.

" What the 'ell 've you been doin'? " said the Bo'sn as I climbed breathless up the steel ladder and emerged into the warm air above.

" Earning my shilling a week," I said.

And I honestly believed for a minute or two that I had.

They covered the hatchways again and washed the decks with a hose. On the starboard side was a heap of small rejected fish, all waste, and a slippery confusion of fishy entrails—flaccid, twisted, pink tubes, delicate fleshy organs wrenched out and splashed in bloody disorder about the deck. These retreated into the scuppers before the jet of the hose, slithered out of the freeing ports and floated astern, staining the water with little brown and crimson clouds. Astern the Kittiwakes, grey with black-pencilled wings, screamed and swooped and fought in chattering hosts, rose up in clouds, settled down and pursued us again, scavenging from the clean surface of the sea all traces of our handiwork.

In another hour the trawl would be in again. During all this time it had been sweeping along the sea floor gathering in its harvest. Soon there would be another mound of goggling gaping death to be gone through with the knife and with tough skilful fingers. But not just yet. There was time for a smoke. There was time for a nice cup of tea. Or a sleep. Time to read an old magazine or an old letter. One by one they went below, lighting fags and pulling off their oilskins.

Time for a smoke.

CHAPTER XIV

HARRY spoke so seldom and, when he did, it was in so melancholy a tone that I decided quite early in the trip that there must be something on his mind. A woman in Grimsby, I thought. A love affair in Blyth. "I dunno," said Tom. "He's always like that, I reckon. Don't never seem to say much." Harry was a stout rosy-faced man whose chin and cheeks were never free, even when he was dressed for going ashore, from a black stubble of beard. It seemed to be a kind of irreducible minimum which no razor could overcome. But no one on board the *Lincoln Star* seemed to know him very well.

We had been on the fishing grounds off the North Cape about a day when Harry cut his hand rather badly on a steel wire. These hawsers are always dangerous to handle with the naked palm because they tend to become frayed and stranded as they grow old so that small broken strands of steel wire stick out from them here and there like thorns. Harry grasped the jilson wire with his bare palm at the moment the winch drums began to move. The wire tightened and ran through his hand so that a small projecting strand tore his palm. Harry swore suddenly and violently.

"What's the matter, Harry?"

"Cut me hand."

"Careless b——. Serve you right!"

Harry said nothing but stood for a while wrapping

his wounded palm in a rag that had once been a handkerchief but was now black with dirt. Then he went on with his work.

It was most unfortunate about Harry's hand but just how unfortunate it was we did not realize for a good many days. There was very little time for anyone but me to realize anything. There was no time to realize how tired you were or how much you needed sleep, nor how much you would like to wash or shave or put on a clean shirt. For our luck had turned. Between hauls, after one lot of fish had been stowed and the deck washed, there was barely time to get a bite to eat or to fill your mug in the galley or go below for a moment before there was a shout of "Heave away!" and the winches began rattling again, filling the fore-deck with clouds of white steam. Soon it would begin all over again, a new mountain of cold dead fish to wade through.

We never lost sight of our dan buoy that marked the place where we had taken our first rich haul. By day we could always see its dark fluttering flag and by night its winking pin-prick of light in the vast blackness. Sometimes it was a tiny and distant dot a mile or so away across the water so that you could only just make it out with the glasses (a present to the Skipper long ago, prisms broken so that you saw two circular fields and had to shut one eye). At other times the buoy went riding past us near at hand, fluttering and swaying bravely up and down from hollow to crest and down again.

Every time the trawl came in on these grounds it was heavy and bulging with fish. It poured forth with a roar upon the deck a flapping, slithering multitude. And each time the Skipper said, " Good-oh! " and went shadow-boxing round the wheel-house. The men worked with an intent and silent concentration. The conversation in the gutting pound became sparser and sparser and their hands worked more and more swiftly, ripping, tearing, flinging aside and reaching out to the ever-diminishing, ever-renewed mountain of cold corpses about their feet. When each pile was finished, washed and stowed below, and when the decks had been washed down, the men went aft in silence to fill the tea mugs that never left their sides. Then they went for'ard at once to get a little sleep in the half-hour, maybe, before the trawl came in again.

" How long, Jim? "

" Twenty minutes, about."

" Not longer? "

" No, not more. I'll call you out."

In twenty minutes out they came again, pulling on their oilskins, tightening the bands around their wrists, pulling on sou'-westers to begin it all once more.

" Heave up, men. Hup! "

" Jilson! "

" Come up, ye bastard! "

Hour after hour, day after day, night after night they worked and the Skipper gave them no rest. Sometimes in deep sea trawlers, when the men have been working three days and nights, perhaps, at a stretch, the Skipper may order the men two or three hours' sleep. When the deckies get tired the work slows down, the fish are less carefully gutted and washed, tangles and mishaps with the gear become more frequent so that valuable gear and equally valuable time are lost. The younger deckies, the learners, may fall forward on their hands and knees at last, dead asleep among the fish. It is best to call a halt then, give them a spell below and not shoot the trawl again until the crew have had a rest. But the men of the *Lincoln Star* got no rest. We must make up for lost time. There had been a week wasted off the North Cape during which we had done no good at all. We could, of course, have stayed an extra week at sea upon the grounds to make up for that. We should have run a bit short of food though that was not the reason why the Skipper was anxious to get back within the twenty-one days. There were two much better reasons. In the first place, if he remained out longer the fish caught earlier in the trip would be stale by the time he got it home and would not fetch such a good price in the market. And in the second place there were those urgent wires that kept arriving from Grimsby—" Please return immediately. Very anxious. Lucy." So he drove the crew and gave them no rest at all.

" Come on there! Look lively! "

" Now then—smartly up with it! Blimey! Like a bloody funeral this evening."

But he gave himself no rest either. He never slept and seldom ate and the red stubble on his chin grew into a fuzz that hid his throat. Yet his good humour never failed him. He sang his snatches of song ceaselessly in the bridge-house, poised his dividers over the thumbed and pencilled chart, ran down to the fore-deck whenever the catch came in and said, " Good-oh! We're not doin' so bad. Over she goes again! " And then once more the winches rattled bearing the great bag down into the darkness of the sea.

The men were content for all their hard work and their fatigue. It was their job. Their silence was the quiet of men concentrating on familiar work. With weariness and back-ache, raw chafed hands and broken nails the good money was coming in. Billie's motor-bike, Tom's new set of teeth, Sambo's new suit. These were remembered in the moments below but forgotten in hard labour during the hours on deck. Whenever I came down to the fore-deck they would look up without pausing, their busy hands moving all the time, and say, " Hallo, Dick! Still at it, you see. What d'ye think to this fishin' now? "

But Harry never looked up or smiled. He worked slowly and painfully but doggedly, for a hot drumming in the palm of his hands kept pace with the beating of his own heart.

The two centre compartments of the fish-room were full. Now the fish were being laid on the shelves in the after compartment, the smaller ones packed irregularly in layers of ice and the larger ones laid neatly head to tail, like huge sardines, hard and stiff as wood. When the after compartment was full, as it would be in a few days at the present rate, they would begin on the fore compartment where Sambo, with his relentless shovel, had eroded away a large part of the cliff of ice.

At the end of four or five days continuous fishing

on the Langanes grounds we suddenly ceased to get good catches. The men got through the gutting and washing and stowing more quickly. They were able to sleep longer below. We picked up the dan buoy and moved south down the east coast. The Skipper, in this moment of respite, shaved off his beard in the little water-logged lavatory adjoining his cabin and came up thereafter with a smooth pink face and his hair oiled down as it had not been for nearly a fortnight. The change had a startling and reviving effect upon him, much more so, it would seem, than hours of sleep. He minced mockingly up and down the bridge with his hand on his hip, made boxing passes at me, played football with an orange, scrambled down to his cabin again and returned with a handful of Burmah cheroots. Presently the air in the wheelhouse was thick and blue with the smoke of our thanksgiving sacrifice. The Skipper was in high spirits. And fifty miles off Seydisfjördur we struck lucky again and put the buoy down once more.

"We'll get fourteen hundred quid this trip, I shouldn't wonder," said the Skipper. To hell with the war! To hell with Hitler! Lucy must worry a bit longer. The fishing was good.

So it was particularly unfortunate about Harry's hand.

While we were on the fishing grounds the Skipper never used his cabin so I slept there. I never undressed but took off only my coat and trousers and my sea-boots. I used my coat and trousers as a pillow. The Skipper, during his rare moments of rest, lay down without undressing at all on the settee in the chart-room. When I came up the companion one morning on to the bridge, too late for breakfast, I found the Skipper, Jim and the Bo'sn in conclave in the wheel-house. Sparks, and Tom at the wheel, were perhaps in the position of unofficial observers at the conference. I made a third and still more unofficial observer. Their deliberations had an air of extreme gravity.

"Well," said the Bo'sn. "This is just the sort of thing that would go and happen just as we're gettin' some fish."

"Where it is, like," said Jim, "if he'd come along at once, like, and had it dressed proper, see, likely this wouldn't 'ave happened. As it is he'll have to to go to a doctor from what I can see of it. It looks a pretty nasty sort of place to me."

"Well, it's his own bloody fault," said the Skipper. "It's his own fault for not payin' proper attention to it from the start. One thing I do know. I'm not goin' to leave off fishin' now to take him in to a doctor. It'd take me half a day to get into Seydisfjord from here and another half-day to get him seen to up at the hospital and the ship cleared, and another half-day to get out on the grounds again. Maybe two days lost. Unless I had a man bloody well dyin' on me I wouldn't do it, not as things are. We've wasted enough time steaming already. I'll take 'im in when we're full and not before. It's his own fault, anyway."

"It's like this 'ere, I reckon," said Tom, leaning upon the spokes of the wheel and gazing ruminatively at his matchstick. "It's like this 'ere. He tried to keep on workin' as long as he could stick it. Thought you might lay 'im off if he came to you, see? So 'e kept on workin'! Didn't want to leave us chaps short-handed on deck. Well, now it's got poisoned and gone bad on 'im, like, and 'e can't work. Lyin' on his bunk moanin', 'e was, last spell below and he's all swollen up terrible under the arm 'ere. That's what it was, though. Didn't want to leave us short-handed on deck."

"Silly bastard!" said the Bo'sn.

"He'll just have to lay off now," the Skipper concluded, "and keep it properly dressed. I'll take him into Seydisfjord to the hospital when we're full, but not before. Shouldn't be more than three or four days now. Wouldn't do more if I had the Duchess o' Kent aboard here with a poisoned hand. How's her head, Tom?"

"North ten east."

"Keep her there!"

Harry's hand had become septic. Since he had taken no care of it at all and had not washed or dressed it in any way since the accident happened several days ago this was not very surprising. The wound was continually opening afresh as he worked. Then he wrapped a sweat cloth round his palm and went on working. Now, hour after hour, the pulse of it beat and throbbed like hammer blows and he went about with a fire like a live coal in the palm of his hand that never cooled but grew hotter and hotter. Under his arm a tender swelling had appeared so that he could scarcely move it. But he said nothing and stuck it. He worked more and more slowly on deck until presently the pain became unbearable. Then he appeared on the bridge with his round red face looking more than usually sorrowful, rather as a child looks when it is about to confess to some fearful enormity like stealing jam.

" Afraid I'll have to lay off, Skipper. It's my hand. I can't use it no more. Could I have a dressing out o' the medicine chest? "

" Aye. Why the hell didn't you come up and get one before? "

" I dunno, really. I thought, like, it might be O.K. in a day or so. Didn't like to leave 'em short-handed on deck, like."

Under the chart-room table there was a large black box which had excited my evil curiosity for a long time. A telescope, I thought. But no—if it were a telescope it would surely have been shown to me long ago with just the same pride as that with which I was shown the sextant, living in idleness and luxury in its velvet-lined nest below. A barometer? A range finder? No. A gun? Of course—a gun. For suppressing mutiny and insubordination. Poor thing! It had a pretty poor chance of ever being used. But, yet no. A medicine chest. Why had I never thought of that before? It was dragged out into the wheel-house that morning and stood open now displaying its secrets. Rolls of cotton wool and packets of lint and bandages spilled out over the deck. It was easy enough to gather from its contents what kind of ailments afflict fishermen at sea. The overflowing profusion of cotton wool, bandages and lint showed that the commonest ills were cuts and wounds. There were splints which showed that broken bones and sprains were common enough, though it seemed unlikely that anyone on board would know what to do with the splints. There was a book which told you what to do in most cases and was extremely helpful. " Maintain the pressure on the femoral artery until the Doctor arrives," it said. " Keep the patient still." And there was every conceivable explosive aperient and purge that I had ever heard of. Most of them I had usually vaguely connected with horses. There were various disinfectants none of which, evidently, had ever been used. There were packets of catgut (unopened), scissors, forceps and catheters, bright and new as the day they were made. There was almost everything you needed for first-aid in that useful and compendious box including a clean anaesthetic smell. The only thing lacking was the faintest rudiment of knowledge of first-aid. But every man must be his own physician in a trawler. The Skipper gave Harry a roll of cotton wool, bandages and lint.

" Keep it bandaged and change the lint every day," he said. " We shall be full in a day or so now and I'll take you in to the hospital at Seydisfjord. But not before. You'd better lay off for the rest of the trip."

Harry took the dressings and went below.

" And for Christ's sake wash the bloody thing before you bind it up! " called the Bo'sn after him.

He came up on deck again after some time with his hand in a swathe of linen bandages like a boxing glove.

" Hallo, Harry lad! " they said from the gutting pound, straightening themselves over the fish for a moment. " How's it goin'? "

" Can't grumble," said Harry.

He could have but he didn't. He sat down on a bollard and watched them do the familiar work he could no longer do, a good man forced to be idle. Whenever the trawl came in during the remaining days of the trip Harry would sit there ruefully watching his shipmates at work, his bandaged hand, unskilfully bound up so that it was almost as big as a football, resting on his knee. It throbbed and burned like fire.

" How's the hand, Harry? "

" Not so bad, thanks—considering."

" Blasted nuisance! " said the Skipper on the bridge, seeing him sitting thus. " Landing me short-handed just when we're getting some fish! "

The *Lincoln Star* circled on ceaselessly upon the eastern banks. During the grey or sunlit daylight I watched the trawl come in time after time, helped to haul it over the rail, saw it heave up and swing over the deck to spew forth over and over again its flapping, gaping treasure. It was always the same, cod, haddock, saithe, ling, cat-fish, plaice. I watched hour after hour the deft tough fingers slit them up and tear the guts out of them, saw the empty disembowelled carcases catapult ceaselessly across the deck into the washing pound and disappear presently in baskets into the fish-room below. I thought, " For God's sake let's stop this and get home." But I never said it. Sometimes I went below and saw how the cold wooden bodies were stacked all around in close-packed tiers. They filled all the shelves now up to the deck-heads. Sambo had reduced the precipice of ice at the fore end and had spread it like a shroud over all those green and silver corpses from which the lustre of life had long ago departed. I gave a hand, of sorts, down in the fish-room, heaving the cold, flabby, alkaline-smelling things about and winning, in exchange for chilled fingers, a comfortable compensating moral glow inside. And over and over again I saw the trawl sink away into the dark water out of sight, a hungry mouth agape for more and more and still more, to return in two or three hours bulging with the curve and gleam of trapped silver bodies, gaping mouths and goggling eyes protruding through the meshes.

But all this became so familiar and so constantly repeated, so unvarying was the routine that went on day and night, that it presently lost interest for me and became only a sort of background to life like the changing colour of the sky, the motion of the ship, the alternation of daylight and darkness. It became the setting for the uproar that was going on in my own mind, itself the reflection of other happenings very far away and yet very near, and to me of much more desperate urgency than all the cod and haddock on all the grounds of Iceland. "In the event of a gas attack," said the B.B.C. in an even confident voice, "wrap the child in a blanket and carry it as quickly as possible to the nearest shelter." That was in London, the ugly, uncomfortable, well-beloved city where I lived and was at home. And the cod and the haddock came sprawling down upon the deck for the hundred and fiftieth time. "Good-oh! We're doin' fine." At night I could bear the roar and rattle of the winches in my troubled sleep, the distant shouts of "Jilson! Heave up!", the rasp of wires along the hull, the quickening and slowing of the engines, beating like a heart, in obedience to the remote tinkle of the engine telegraph.

Harry and I shared a magnificent and forlorn loneliness, the loneliness of having nothing at all to do in the midst of people hard at work. We were united by our common longing for the moment when the trawl should disgorge itself upon the deck for the last time. Only the difference in our reasons for that longing made a slight barrier between us.

"Shan't be sorry when we're full," said Harry one day, sitting on his usual bollard.

"Nor shall I. I'm fed up. I want to get home. How's the hand? Is it still paining you?"

"Aye. It is an' all. Can't get no sleep at night. 'Ere——" he leant towards me conspiratorially, "when's 'e packin' up, d'you know?"

"No. Can't be too soon for me."

"Nor me neither."

And soon the others began, occasionally at first but by degrees more often, to ask the same question, "When's he packin' up?"

The monotony of these days, the hard work and the long hours, the lack of sleep, the grinding routine, were beginning to tell on them. More and more, during their often interrupted meals, they began to talk of what they would do when they got back to Grimsby. Those thirty-six hours in port began to appear like the distant prospect of the promised land, limitless and fair but far-off as yet upon the horizon. But within sight. They began to count up what each man's share would be.

"Ten or twelve quid. That ain't bad. Put some o' that on Grimsby Town at the match next Saturday. They're playin' at home. It should be a good game, should that."

Billie remembered his motor-bike again. Tom remembered his approaching visit to the dental hospital. His courage was dwindling, I noticed, as the visit approached.

"Maybe I'll go if I win something on the match," he said.

And always they asked, "When's he packin' up?"

Jim came into the saloon rather late for tea on the seventeenth day out from Grimsby. He had come straight up from the fish-room and there clung to him still that alkaline, pungent, fishy smell. "We're not far from full now," he said. "One side of the fore compartment and then we'll be full. I expect he'll pack up soon. Well, I shan't be sorry to be southward bound myself. I expect my little lot'll be gettin' a bit anxious the way things are, like."

But the Skipper, humming to himself on the bridge, showed no signs of packing up.

That evening, perhaps because the men were tired and not so efficient as they might have been, the trawling warps fouled each other as the trawl went out. They had to haul the gear in again. The otter boards came up to the gallows draped in swathes of torn and tangled netting. They worked in the darkness for several hours to free them, silently, doggedly, swearing occasionally, while the *Lincoln Star* wallowed on the high swell that ran in towards the dark mountains. When at last they had freed the otter boards the net was torn to ribbons. The whole belly of the trawl had been ripped out.

"Luck's gone now," they said. "Likely he'll be packin' up now."

"What'll you do, Skipper?" I said, looking at the torn net spread over the deck. "Are you packing up now?"

"Hell, no. Shoot the port trawl!"

They shot the trawl on the port side, not used as yet this trip. The men obeyed in silence. No one said a word as they paid the net over and heaved the foot-rope up with the port jilson. "Away she goes!" The ship plunged forward as the trawl sank away, sweeping round to port now instead of to starboard, making upon the night sea a left-handed arc of troubled water.

"You don't know me," the Skipper said. "I don't go home till we're full."

I went to bed and heard, through sleep, the often repeated rattle of the winches, the shouts and the hiss and clatter of the steering engine every time the helm went over. In the morning the Skipper said, "No luck. Only sixty baskets all night."

"What are you going to do?"

"I'm going in towards the land again."

We went in towards the land until we could see

the mountains of the east coast like a wall along the west, streaked with departing snow. We fished there under the coast all day. The men were working slowly now as though in a dream. I heard no word come from them in the gutting pound. Billie did not laugh as he bent down to rip up the bellies of the fish. When they were bringing in the trawl on one occasion I heard Jim's voice raised in anger for the first time.

" Am I the blasted mate or are you then? What the bloody hell d'you think you're playin' at. I give the word, not you! If you want to take charge 'ere, say so. I don't f—— well care. I'll go below! " Tom lit a cigarette and walked away.

But that evening Sparks came out of his cabin into the wheel-house.

" Skipper! " he said. " Your missus on the radio telephone." The Skipper went into the radio cabin and shut the door. For ten minutes he spoke across those miles of sea from his little, weary, rocking ship to his wife in Grimsby. And yet how strange, I thought, that miracles such as this do not diminish distance, as one might expect, but seem to increase it. The closer men come to each other the less they seem able to look each other in the eyes. The more time they save the less they know how to use it. The easier it becomes for them to speak to one another the less they have to say.

In ten minutes the Skipper came out of the radio cabin into the wheel-house again.

" We're packing up," he said.

CHAPTER XV

"It will be well soon now, I think," said the doctor. "I have lanced it and cleaned it up. You must make him to change the dressing, please, every day. It was not good, that hand, I think."

The doctor was an extremely elegant young man who climbed over the dirty, fishy rail of the *Lincoln Star* wearing a suit of a becoming shade of mauve, a grey hat and grey suede gloves. He smoked a cigarette in a long holder. He looked like Copenhagen's idea of Gilbert the Filbert, and was quite the last thing I had expected to see on arriving in the land of fire and water, of heroic legend and of song, of Egill Skallagrimsson and Grettyr the Outlaw.

"You are going home—yes?" He spoke English almost perfectly.

"Yes, we're going home," said the Skipper. "Mind the paint."

The Sergeant in his capacity of cook-steward-valet had conceived the idea of repainting the Skipper's lavatory. "Ah, make it a bit proper for port, see?" He had begun this self-imposed labour on the way into port that afternoon when the fishing was finished and his hideously unskilful handiwork was still wet and gleaming. The doctor, washing his hands in the lavatory, leapt out as though he had been given an electric shock. On the beautiful suit were shameful smudges of white paint.

"It is nothing," he said. But it was obvious that it was a great deal. "What do you go home for—war? It is better to stay here, I think."

I thought so, too. It was a clear still evening. The smoke from the little wooden houses of Seydisfjördur went straight up into the air and hung as a smoky web above the harbour, slung between the steep barren mountains whose grassy skirts walled in the narrow fjord. The shadows crept slowly up the mountain sides until only their rocky summits stood in the evening sun, which seemed to linger there as though not eager to depart. It was the kind of evening when sounds seem to carry a great distance. As we lay at the jetty the pleasant and familiar noises that give a community to all places where people live and work, however far apart and different they may otherwise be, came faintly to us across the water—the rattle of a motor-car, the sound of distant voices, the bark of a dog, the clack of oars moving leisurely in row-locks. And over all the screaming of the gulls that scavenged up and down the water-front. A few fair-haired men and boys stood on the jetty and stared at us in silence with faces as expressionless as those of cows. They were poorly dressed and their mouths hung vacuously open.

There are only two or three towns in Iceland. Reykjavik is the capital on the south-west coast and Akureyri, on the north coast, is the second largest town in the island. Seydisfjördur, at the head of its long narrow arm of the sea upon the eastern coast, is the third. There is a road of sorts, I believe, from Reykjavik to Akureyri and Seydisfjördur but it runs all round the western and northern coasts and is hardly what we should call a road, so that the main communication between Seydisfjördur and the outside world is by sea. But it did not seem to me as though this little lost community would have much use for the outside world in any case or would care whether it could communicate with it or not. Yet a large tank labelled " Shell," the German consulate, surmounted by its sinister black eagle, and the German tobacco I bought at the little shop all assured me that the outside world does manage to penetrate even here. The tobacco was as issued to the German army. I smoked some and threw the rest away feeling even more sorry for the German people than I did before. The people of Seydisfjördur live almost entirely by fishing. They eat much of the fish they catch, splitting them and drying them in the sun. As you walk down the little street that leads to the head of the harbour split dried cod-fish and haddock are all about you laid out on frames. Every house has its store of them impaled upon spikes outside the door. The fishermen's boats are drawn up on the beach and the men sit mending their nets and salute you as you pass.

There is an excitement and a sense of adventure in setting foot for the first time in a foreign country. It is one of life's sensations which the years do not diminish. I remember so well my astonishment on landing in France for the first time. I cannot imagine what I had expected but I suppose every Englishman, who goes for the first time to that mysterious and outlandish place known as "abroad", undertakes the journey rather as though he were making an expedition into the land of the head-hunters. Yet here, I found, the grass was green and the sky was blue and the people walked miraculously upright upon two legs. Nevertheless, and this seems still more amazing to me now than it did then, the place was indubitably, undeniably and excitingly French. There was a lot more noise than I was accustomed to. People went about smelling of garlic, which was unheard of where I came from, and everything had an air of untidy, unpainted, meretricious elegance about it. Where France was ugly, and that seemed to be almost everywhere on first acquaintance, it was quite a different ugliness from that of England. Since the moment of that strange discovery the aspects and characters of countries, stamped upon the landscape and even on the very meanest buildings by the mode of life, the daily thoughts and aspirations of the common people, have seemed to me to be the true joy of travel. The vast grandeur and desolate loneliness of nature are quite without significance if mankind has not stamped his imprint upon them. I do not want to see the Grand Canyon or the Canadian Rockies or the Amazon jungle. I would rather see Chicago or Blackpool during Wakes week. So when I go to Paris I take a fleeting and respectful glance at the Louvre, half an hour at the Invalides and spend the rest of the day wandering about the streets marvelling at the Frenchness of it all. On the last occasion, while I was marvelling moonily in the Place de la Concorde, a young man who said he was Swiss invited me to accompany him to a place where girls from the Folies Bergères bathe in champagne for the delectation of the bloated rich like me. Poor tired girls—after the feathers and the sequins twice nightly! I told him that, diverting as such a spectacle must be, it hardly fitted with my mood so he offered me something even more bizarre. But as I walked with Sambo and Jack Johnson down the rough and dusty street of Seydisfjördur no one made me any such alluring proposals. A small boy on a white pony rode past, turning back to stare at us over the pony's rump. An old man with a long beard sitting at his door lifted his hand and Jack Johnson expressed desire for a slatternly girl with very dirty bare legs. And yet in some degree I caught the Icelandic flavour of this untidy little town. It was a robust, fishy, Scandinavian flavour, tinged with smoke and things that rotted on the shore. There was a Scandinavian flavour about the gabled wooden houses with their steep roofs, the strange, unlikely, near-Scandinavian words printed here and there and the sing-song voices of the people miraculously pronouncing them. It was foreign and exciting and tantalising. And we had so little time to stay. Jim had called after us, " Don't be gone long now! We're sailing in half an hour! "

" One-eyed sort of a hole this! " said Sambo, looking around in disgust.

" Well, I don't know," I said.

It seemed to me at that moment to be an immense advantage to live in a one-eyed hole and to be a member of a one-eyed community. No one wanted to take your one eye from you. Perhaps, I thought, it will be in these one-eyed holes that civilization will survive when all those who despise them so much have killed and ruined each other fighting about how many eyes each ought to have. Then a race of men will be left who will live as men should live and as they once lived, by wresting their living from the fruitful earth or the abounding sea, eating when they feel hungry, sleeping when they feel tired, making love when they feel passionate, working hard all their lives under the sky and dying at last to be buried under the good earth they have tended. Yet how devoutly I hoped I should never live like that myself. Yet this was how the Icelanders lived, I felt—hard, dangerous, difficult but happy lives. The weather was their only enemy. They were tall and strong and fair. They greeted you frankly in the street. They stared at you unabashed and did not drop their eyes. Their faces, blank and expressionless as cows, told how great was their vegetable contentment. But their clothes were shabby and ill-fitting and all the women I set eyes on seemed to be slatterns. So perhaps they were not really so much to be envied after all.

We only stayed a few hours in Seydisfjord. The presence of the *Lincoln Star* at the jetty was quite obviously an event, for quite a crowd of men and boys, hands in pockets, collected on the jetty and stared and stared. Down in his cabin the Skipper was doing the honours by the elegant young doctor and the agent, who was a stout jolly man with a red face. They were both Danes. The Skipper produced the last bottle of beer we had bought in Blyth and handed round his pungent Burmah cheerots. We might have been a visiting warship, such ceremony did the two Danes observe in the tiny panelled cubby-hole. They bowed, lifted their glasses, caught your eye, held it, and said "*Skål*," bowed and put their glasses down again. On the deck the crew of the *Lincoln Star*, not to be outdone, leaned against the casing in a row, their hands in the pockets of their fear-nought trousers, and stared stolidly back at the silent company on the jetty, the Bo'sn smoking and spitting tobacco shreds, Tom chewing his matchstick and Sandy the corner of his sweat cloth. No one said a word. It was difficult to know whose mental processes were working the faster, those of the Icelanders or the Englishmen. Presently the Bo'sn spat on the deck.

"Wouldn't go ashore in this miserable bloody 'ole," he said. "Can't even get a drink here!"

But Sambo was more adventurous. "Comin' ashore for a walk, Dick?"

So Sambo and Jack Johnson and I walked up the little street of wooden houses, trim and neat with the split fish drying outside their doors, and their little patches of soil growing potatoes. That was all I saw of Iceland—these little gabled wooden houses and these steep green mountains that swept up behind them to rocky summits bare against the blue sky.

We sailed when the sun had gone from the fjord and the mountain tops were no longer tipped with light. Against the dark slopes the lights of the town began to come out, making long quivering columns of brightness in the water. The shadowy mountains fell away from the *Lincoln Star* as she slipped down the fjord. She left a long immobile trail of smoke behind her above her troubled wake. A light flashed at the entrance to the fjord. The stars were out. I shall not forget the calm peace of that tiny distant city, lost and lonely and remote, where the people live hard and work hard and never think about anything at all. Their hand is against no man and no man's hand is against them.

CHAPTER XVI

THE covers were on the hatches. The otter-boards were shipped inboard once again. The port trawl lay stowed snug along the scuppers and the winches were covered up. In three days we should be in Grimsby again. In this hour of leisure and warm sunshine, during which the coast of Iceland faded away upon the north-west, the two short days of life and liberty that lay ahead seemed like a whole eternity.

The deckies were sitting in a row, their backs against the casing, their legs sprawling over the deck, mending the belly of the starboard trawl which had been torn the day we stopped fishing. It was a bright and sunny morning. To the north-west the snow-streaked mountains faded away until you could not tell whether it were a line of mountains or a line of cloud you saw upon the northern horizon. The *Lincoln Star* moved gently upon the swell. No speck stained the pure sky and the sea was glassy smooth except for the oily swell that ran up out of the south.

When Sparks came down from the bridge and said he had received a gale warning, everyone laughed. "Go on! Tell us another!" The expanse of net, patched with the new white belly they were sewing in, billowed over the deck around them. Their mugs of tea were by their sides.

Now that the fishing was over the Skipper had retaken possession of his cabin and I was sleeping once again uneasily on the settee in the chart-room, where

I had slept on passage north. Only on such uncomfortable occasions does one become fully aware of the existence of shoulders, hips and elbows. When I awoke on the first morning of our homeward voyage, aching in every one of my apparently innumerable knobs and protuberances, I heard the radio in Sparks' cabin next door sonorously proclaiming peace. I went out into the chart-room half dressed to listen, forgetting the supreme indignity of shirt tails. When I had dressed I went down to where the men were sitting on the main deck in the sun.

"The war's off!" I said.

Their hands were busy, going automatically through the familiar movements—over, under, through. But in their imaginations the crew of the *Lincoln Star* were already ashore in Grimsby. For them the trip was over. There were no other trips ahead, no more sleepless days and nights of hard work, no more fatigue, no more cold and wet, no flapping slithering heaps of corpses any more. They were not interested in the war or in the fact that it was off. Only Tom said, "Good job, too! Who wants a war, anyway?" and turned to his companions.

"Comin' to see the match against Leeds this Saturday? Grimsby sh'd do all right with their new centre-forward, I reckon. Sh'd be a good game an' all. Maybe I'll put two or three quid on before the old woman gets it."

"What about those teeth of yours?" I reminded him.

"Oh aye! There's time enough for that, though."

"I'll be up at Sam's Saturday evening," said

Billie. "There's a blonde tart I could do with up there. So I could an' all. You remember 'er the night before we sailed?"

"What—that one? Well, you can 'ave it. I'd rather take the old woman to the Tivoli."

"Ah! You was payin' enough attention that evenin'. So you was!"

"Me? I know a game worth two o' that."

"What about that bike?" I said.

"Oh aye! I'll be putting a bit by, never you fear! I'll have a good time first though. There's some prime tarts in Grimsby, Dick. What about comin' ashore with us the night we get in. I'll get you one."

I made a rather vague reply to this cordial invitation. I was sitting on one of the bobbins of the foot-rope, stowed along the starboard scuppers. Every one of that line of iron spheres was polished bright as silver now from two weeks grinding along the sand and stones and rocks of the sea-floor. The wooden discs between the spheres were worn into the shape of truncated cones. Bright as silver too gleamed the under sides of the metal shoes with which the otter boards were shod. It had been a good trip. Down in the fish-room was about fourteen hundred pounds clear profit which would be shared among the crew. As their share the deckies would get about twelve pounds each in addition to their wages. If they had been coming home with doubloons from the Spanish main, with all the plundered treasure of the east, they would have spent it all in advance that sunny morning, sitting on the deck while their hands moved automatically at the growing web of new white twine.

And to hear them spending it you would think they were returning after many years to end their days either in the wild pursuit of pleasure or in leisured dignity and well-earned rest.

" Well," said Jim in the saloon. " Soon be seein' my little family now. If we don't get in too late maybe they'll come down to the dock. I'd like you to meet the missus, Dick. 'Tisn't often I talk about my little girl but I would like you to meet 'er."

" I'd like to too, Jim. I hope we'll get in in time."

You could not mistake the suppressed eagerness and excitement in his voice. Already he was at home there by his fireside, there at the focal point of all his thoughts and longings for the past three weeks. And many weeks before that and many more to come. How fortunate or how wise he was! For surely the anticipation of home-coming is the greatest pleasure it affords!

The Sergeant was in great form in these days. To mark the end of fishing and the beginning of the passage home he put on a clean apron and cap. He slapped down a wedge of rice on to my plate with his long spoon, for potatoes had run out some days ago.

" Good stuff! Fills yer out! " the Sergeant said. " Tell yer what—make yer a nice cake this afternoon. Bit o' weddin' cake for the end o' the trip, see! "

At tea time he bore in proudly, under a sheet of cellophane, the last of his masterpieces. The last, that is, that I was ever to grapple with. All the silver balls left in his store had been arranged upon it in whorls and spirals. In pink on the top were the words " For

Auld Lang Syne," and two not very skilfully executed hands locked in a grip of friendship.

" There! " he said. " For old time's sake, that is. Well, don't know if I'll be comin' out next trip. Got to see after the old woman when I get in. That's what I got to do. Ought to 'ave heard how she's gettin' on but I ain't heard nothin'. But that's what I got to do all right—see how she's gettin' on. Ah, poor old girl."

And there was someone waiting for them all in Grimsby. Sparks showed me a snapshot of his girl in Southport whom he hoped to see. " Don't know as I'll marry 'er. She caught me a clip across the side of the 'ead last time I saw 'er. Bloody 'ell! It didn't half hurt! " I was not surprised for she was an Amazonian beauty. In a bathing suit, as the snap showed her, she had a Rubens torso. I should have hated to try conclusions with her. Even Jack Johnson had his old man waiting for him who was black as the ace of spades and would take all his money. So, not for the first time in the trip, I felt a bit out of it and removed from them. This time it was because for them the dreary city of Grimsby had the warmth of home. For me it only signified a bath and a meal with a tablecloth, a place where I would sleep in a bed again. However, that was something. But there was no one waiting for me there. And the places they talked about, the people they hoped to see, the scenes they were living already in their imaginations had no meaning for me. I had no share in their home-coming.

But I was not quite alone in this for, in his bunk

below, the Skipper slept the long deep sleep of utter exhaustion, the light above his head still burning. He had fallen asleep before he could reach his hand up to put it out.

The gale struck the *Lincoln Star* off the Faroes. The sun which had shone so brightly that morning went down behind black banks of cloud. The high tops of the Faroes were hidden in a veil of mist and the darkling sea became stippled with winking flashes of white. There was a rising moan in the rigging. The smoke curled from the funnel in a long torn scarf of black and flattened itself upon the sea astern.

"There's dirty weather coming. We shan't make Grimsby in time to see the match."

"Likely not. It should be a good game, should that. I was lookin' forward to that an' all."

The *Lincoln Star* rolled violently that night. The woodwork in the little chart-room where I tried to sleep creaked and groaned with every plunge she made. In the narrow coffin-like space of the settee between the padded upholstery and the bunk-board which the Sergeant had fixed along the side—"to make it proper and comfortable"—I wedged myself firmly with my knees and my behind and got a firm grip with my elbows. I resigned myself to hours of wakefulness in my little padded mahogany box. For hours I listened to the bows thumping against the rising head-on sea. A moment or so after each thump I would hear the spray spin like shot against the bridge. Then, before the next thump, while she wallowed down, I could hear in the darkness everywhere the tinkling gurgling rush of escaping water. Sometimes I heard the wheel-house door open and the low voices of the helmsmen changing watches. Below there was the muffled hiss and rattle of the steering engine under the bridge, clattering into activity every time the helmsman moved the wheel to keep her on course. But the Skipper in his cabin, next to the steering engine itself, slept on through all the pandemonium which increased around us, his head back and one arm flung upward as though he were about to reach toward the light above him when sleep came upon him.

In the morning the *Lincoln Star* was ploughing and battering through giant grey seas that toppled up before her, curled and fled past trailing veils of foam. As each one approached, dark, menacing, its uncertain lip breaking into white, you thought the pointed bows must strike through it and bring all that curling mass of water down upon the decks. But no! She rode up always, soaring over the advancing crests. In the instant before she plunged down again you could see a dark panorama of mountain and valley, streaked with white, frothing to the horizon. Then the bows, rushing downwards so that the horizon seemed to be drawn up over the sky, met the next charging wall of darkness with a bump and a lurch and all the fore part of the ship became a driving whirl of white that spun against the bridge like hail, blotting out the world. White water streamed from the fo'c'sle head, creamed about the fore-deck and gushed from the freeing ports. And the foremast swung continuously and evenly through the sky like a pendulum. The horizon rose and fell, rose and fell, showing now all flying clouds to the zenith and now only the furious, flecked, dark water. The men slid and ducked and scurried along the fore-deck clutching a life line that ran from the fo'c'sle door to the lee side of the casing. But since the wind was almost dead ahead the casing afforded scarcely any lee and when you came out of the wheel-house door on to the narrow bridge-deck the wind knocked the breath out of your body for a moment or two. Jack Johnson, coming slowly along the deck with newly filled mugs of tea, leant forward against the wind which flattened his stubborn black hair on his head, whipped little spurts of tea from the tops of the mugs and flung them behind him.

" What about comin' in the galley. Nice and warm in there! "

It was. All the pots and pans clinked together on their hooks and swung back and forth and sideways, winking in the light of the galley fire. In the saucepan in which the Sergeant was stirring something over the stove the steaming liquid kept tilting up to the edge and dropping over to disappear upon the hot iron with a hiss and a sizzle of steam.

" Garn up, ye bastard! " shouted the Sergeant into the saucepan. He was bending over the stove, holding on to the rail above his head with one hand, stirring with the other what I took to be soup in the saucepan with a long spoon. He stood with his feet wide apart wedged against the slats in the deck. He bent first one knee and then the other to the bucketing movement that his galley was making around him.

" Any tea, old soldier? "

" Aye. Made a new pot. Weather like this yer want a mug o' tea. Ah well! Never mind. It'll be beer Saturday. You come along o' me Saturday night. I know where you can get it after hours, see. I know a place all right. You come along o' me."

" Don't you go with 'im," said Billie, fixing himself in the galley doorway with one knee and his back while he drank his tea. " Get you into bad company, he will."

Billie was trimming coal again watch and watch with Sambo. His face was black once more with circles beneath his eyes. His skin beneath the torn singlet he had discarded a fortnight ago was ebony as a negro's. He smelt lustily of sweat and coal dust. Sambo was on watch now and if you went along the central alleyway that led through the deckies' mess, past the saloon, and past the after cabins to the engine-room door you could hear him singing in the stokehold above the whine of pumps and the pulse and throb of the engines.

" Me get into bad company? " said the Sergeant with virtuous indignation. " Not me! You never saw me in bad company yet. You come with me Saturday. 'Ave a good time, you an' me. Takes an old soldier to show yer round. They all know me in Grimsby. Sergeant Mace—that's me. They all know me."

" Been thrown out of every pub in Grimsby," said Billie and made a feint as though to ward off an expected blow. They both laughed.

" You don't want to take no notice of 'im," said the

Sergeant, jerking his thumb over his shoulder as he bent over his stove. " Don't know what he's bleedin' well talkin' about, he don't. You come with me down to Sam's. Good sport, old Sam. Same company, see—Sam and me. Both together in France, we was. You ask 'im what he thinks o' Sergeant Mace. You ask Sam." He straightened himself and squared his shoulders. He knew how he stood with Sam.

Sparks came into the galley with a telegram in his hand. His long dark hair was blown forward over his eyes. He smoothed it back with his hand as he gave the telegram to the Sergeant who stopped stirring the unidentified liquid in the saucepan and wiped his hands on his apron before taking it. We guessed what was in the message and said nothing. He read it through several times with his legs wide apart, braced against the slats, his knees bending to the rolling of the ship. His lips moved slightly as he read. Presently he stuffed the paper into the pocket of his blue drill trousers and turned back to the stove. He was silent for a long time, stirring the saucepan.

" Ah well," he said at last. " Ah well. It's a new old woman for me all right. Poor old girl. Poor old girl. Aye."

Down in the saloon we ate the last meals of the trip, holding our plates right up under our chins for fear of spilling everything into our laps. Whenever the little saloon went up and up like a lift we could feel the propeller shaft racing under our feet before all of us, sitting round the table, came rushing headlong down again. The dingy bottles and pots and tins chattered together in the middle of the table.

By now the Duchess of Devonshire in her Gainsborough hat was plastered all over the bulkheads so that there was no room for any more of her. The spring flowers in their little sconces had thick layers of dust on them which dimmed their lustre a little but did not diminish their charm. During these last meals in the *Lincoln Star* a feeling of hopelessness and melancholy would come over me whenever I looked round at the little company that had somehow so easily and so quickly become my world. These were simple people who knew me now and accepted me. After three short weeks I knew them all better and more intimately than I knew many people I had known for years ashore. Yet in a day or so they would all be like figures in a dream, wiped out of my life as you wipe figures from a blackboard. Only by writing them down, as I have written them down here, has it been possible to conjure up the sound of their voices, the touch of their rough hands and to see before me once again their good and ugly faces. Late at night when I put my pen down the traffic of London has stopped. Only a last taxi rattles home. Footsteps sound upon the pavement and die away. For a moment it is almost as though I heard again the husky, cheerful, blasphemous voices of those Englishmen.

" Have another mug of this bloody poison, Dick? "

" What d'ye think to this fishin' now, lad? "

On the faces of the men that stood around in groups in Riby Square the neon lights shone yellow, blue and red. They lit their dull eyes and filled their faces with a colour that did not belong there. The traffic and the Saturday night crowds, cloth-capped, stocky and silent, wove in and out over the pavements and across the street.

"Match result—final!" shouted the newsboy on the corner. One after the other the people paid their penny, paused, turning to the back page, and disappeared into the ceaselessly shifting crowds.

"Aye—it was a grand game was that!"

"He's a good lad, is that centre-forward o' the Town's."

A little group of women separated themselves from the glaring, clanging main street, and walked down the dark side turnings towards the dock.

"She's late," said one.

"Aye. There's a right gale blowin' outside. They told me up at the office she'd be late this evenin'."

"He's missed the match, has my Tom."

"Good job too. He can keep 'is money now like my Jim."

The dock was silent. The great covered sheds where the thousands of boxes of fish were sold every morning were deserted echoing spaces under the quiet lights. Long trembling columns of light shimmered in the dark water of the basin. The *Northern Queen* lay silent at the jetty. Her mooring ropes creaked a little and her condenser water gushed softly with a noise that made the silence greater. No one was aboard her. The women stood on the quay in a little group under an arc light, not speaking, holding their clothes buttoned tight up to their necks.

The *Lincoln Star* had battered her way down the Yorkshire coast all day. She plunged and reared and bucked while the foam flew in a smother over her bows and poured in cascades from her fo'c'sle head.

"Hard luck missin' the bloody match," said Tom. "Might a' made a bit."

"Must a' been a good game," said the Bo'sn rolling a cigarette.

"Haven't been home to see Grimsby Town play for eighteen months. Ah well, better luck next time."

They were wearing their shore-going clothes again, blue suits, clean shirts, cloth caps. They might have been part of the crowd of several cheering thousands that saw Grimsby Town win that afternoon. But for a somewhat uncharitable act of God they would have been part of it. Sparks appeared, after a secret and devotional half-hour with the door of his cabin demurely locked, shaved and brilliantined in his shabby but natty grey suit with the double-breasted waistcoat. The Skipper too was sleek and oiled once more. And I was in my incongruous grey flannels with hair that made a most undecorative fringe over my collar at the back.

It was a pitch dark night. The white charging seas ran past like wild ghosts, rushing up out of darkness ahead and hissing off into darkness astern, but far off ahead there was a confusion of tiny points of light like jewels, shimmering in a long line to southward.

"Good old Grimsby!"

"Will the wife be down to meet you, Jim?"

"Not likely, this time o' night. Hope not, anyway. She oughtn't to be waitin' around like, night like this. Not but what she usually does come down to meet me, see, if she knows what time we're gettin' in, like. But bein' as late as we are it's more than likely she'll wait up at home. 'Course, I'd like 'er to come down in a manner o' speakin'. . . ."

The lights enlarged and brightened before us, growing slowly apart and stringing themselves as we watched along the whole southern skyline. The night blackness all round us was presently pricked with bright points of light that glowed and winked and shifted or burnt still and steady.

" That's Cleethorpes there, see? You can see the lights of the pier now at the end there. That'll be the Fun Fair there in the middle. That's Grimsby further along like. You can see the dock gates where them green lights are, see? "

Grimsby drew slowly nearer, opening out before us like a great glittering flower. The plunging roll of the *Lincoln Star* ceased as she came into the Humber River and threaded her way between the flashing buoys. The sea flattened out. Only the wild south-westerly gale still raced shrieking through the rigging and beat against the windows of the wheel-house. In the medley of steady lights before us across the dark ruffled water some green ones shone. They were beckoning us in.

" Slow ahead! " said the Skipper. " The gates are open."

The water was dark and still within the dock. Here the wind no longer beat around our little box and the silence seemed like sleep. Some of the arc lights rocked a little so that the shadows leapt strangely about the walls.

" She's comin' in," said one of the women.

" Aye, that's her. I can see her masthead lights comin' through the gates now."

" Soon be seein' your Jim now, lass."

Suddenly the silence of the dock was shattered by a voice shouting gigantically through a megaphone.

" Right ahead, *Lincoln Star*. . . . Right ahead as you're goin' behind *Northern Queen*. . . . Right ahead as you're goin'. . . . Right ahead, *Lincoln Star*! "

The men on the fo'c'sle head were ready to throw the lines ashore. On the fore-deck, which was drying now but still shone wet here and there under the lights, their kit-bags were piled against the mast like dummies. In them was all that each man possessed aboard the ship.

" Get ashore, one of you, and take the lines! "

One of them leapt ashore with the lines and the *Lincoln Star* edged gently up to the quay. The women came forward out of the ring of light in which they had been waiting and looked up to the men on the fo'c'sle head.

" Hallo, Tom. You're back at last."

" Aye, lass. We're back at last."

" What sort of a trip? "

" Can't grumble."

" Hallo, Jim."

" Is that you, lass. How're you keepin'? "

One by one with their kit-bags the men climbed up on to the jetty. Some turned and gave me their hands. The hands I gripped were hard and tough as iron. They were scarred and wounded, the nails broken, the fingers always slightly bent. I gripped them one by one and said good-bye.

" Good-bye, Tom. Don't forget about those teeth of yours now. Good-bye, Billie. See you in London may be. Don't forget now—King's Cross Hotel! Good-bye, Old Soldier! Good-bye! Good luck to you! Good luck! "

They moved away under the lights, dark figures passing from darkness into light and back to darkness as they diminished down the long empty quay. Those whose wives had met them went with their women. The others went in pairs. I heard their voices pass away down the jetty.

Outside the dock gates the neon lights shone yellow, blue and red. The busy Saturday night crowds, swirling round the corners of Riby Square, overflowing from the pavement into the road, swallowed up the figures of my friends and drowned their voices.

A newsboy shouted " Match result—Final! " I was quite alone.

CHAPTER XVII

The sky had been washed clean by the storm which had died down. A few fleecy clouds sailed up out of the south-west, rose up over the roofs and masts of Grimsby and floated away across the Humber towards Flamborough Head. A deep-water trawler lay at the south jetty, a small feather of steam hissing at her funnel. Her hatches were battened down. Her trawls were neatly stowed upon the foot-ropes along the rail, her otter-boards lashed inboard. Down in the fore compartment of the fish-room was a new white precipice of ice, loaded yesterday. In the after compartment were high black ramparts of coal.

A young man was hosing down the deck, whistling as he worked. Presently he threw down his hose so that the water ran out of it as a silent crinkled fan upon the deck and bubbled into the scuppers. He went aft and turned into the galley door. Soon from the tall galley chimney a streamer of blue smoke appeared and floated away upon the wind. He filled the large kettle with water and placed it on the newly lighted stove, still whistling to himself. It was nearly half-past seven. They would be along soon.

They came down one by one, blue suits, cloth caps, carrying their kit-bags over their shoulders. He could see them coming a long way off across the basin, out of the shadow of the buildings into the morning sunshine. They said very little to one another, beyond a curt greeting, but climbed silently over the rail and disappeared with their kit-bags for'ard into the fo'c'sle.

"There's a cup o' tea aft if you want one."

"Aye, thanks."

"Any new hands?"

"Aye—one or two."

"Who's not comin' back?"

"Oh, him what hurt his hand last trip. He ain't comin' back. And there's a new cook they tell me. Last bloke lost 'is old woman last trip. Hope to Christ we've got a good 'un!"

Slowly the group of men grew around the galley door. They drank their mugs of tea and lit cigarettes, sitting on the rail or leaning against the lifeboat.

"Well, how d'yer get on ashore?"

"Oh, can't grumble. Lost six quid last Sunday playin' solo. No more solo for me. I got to save up this trip for a new set o' teeth next time in."

"You should 'a been up at Sam's Saturday night. There was a rare lot o' tarts up there. The one I got hold of wants to meet me again next time in but I told 'er no, 'cause I'm saving up for a motor-bike, I said. I ain't put nothin' by towards it this trip but next trip I'm goin' to put by twice the amount. That's what I told 'er and said I couldn't see 'er again. Still—I took 'er address just in case."

"I meant to get a new suit Saturday but we got in so late all the shops were bleedin' well shut. So I spent all the money in the *Albion* on Sunday. Now I got to start an' save up all over again! That's a rum 'un, ain't it? It is an' all." He laughed and scratched the top of his head.

An old-fashioned Daimler drove on to the jetty and two men got out together. One was sleek and fresh from a morning bath and shave. The other wore a natty but shabby grey suit and carried a suitcase. There was a bundle of books under his arm.

The sleek young man looked at his wrist-watch. "Well, we'd better get goin'," he said.

Slowly, silently, without fuss or ceremony of any kind the trawler backed away from the jetty, churning up the water at her stern. As she slid slowly through the dock gates a few men stood by and watched her go. One or two fair-haired Danes in the little seine-netting boats raised their hands. Soon she began to lift gently on the swell that ran into the Humber River from the sea.

"Goin' to sea," said the man at the wheel slowly, "is one of the things that don't seem to come easier with practice. Specially when you're leavin' a little family behind, like."

Soon she was a dot rounding Spurn Head, tiny and far off, her smoke a feather against the sky. Presently she was hull down beyond the buoys and beyond the lightship with its triple flash.

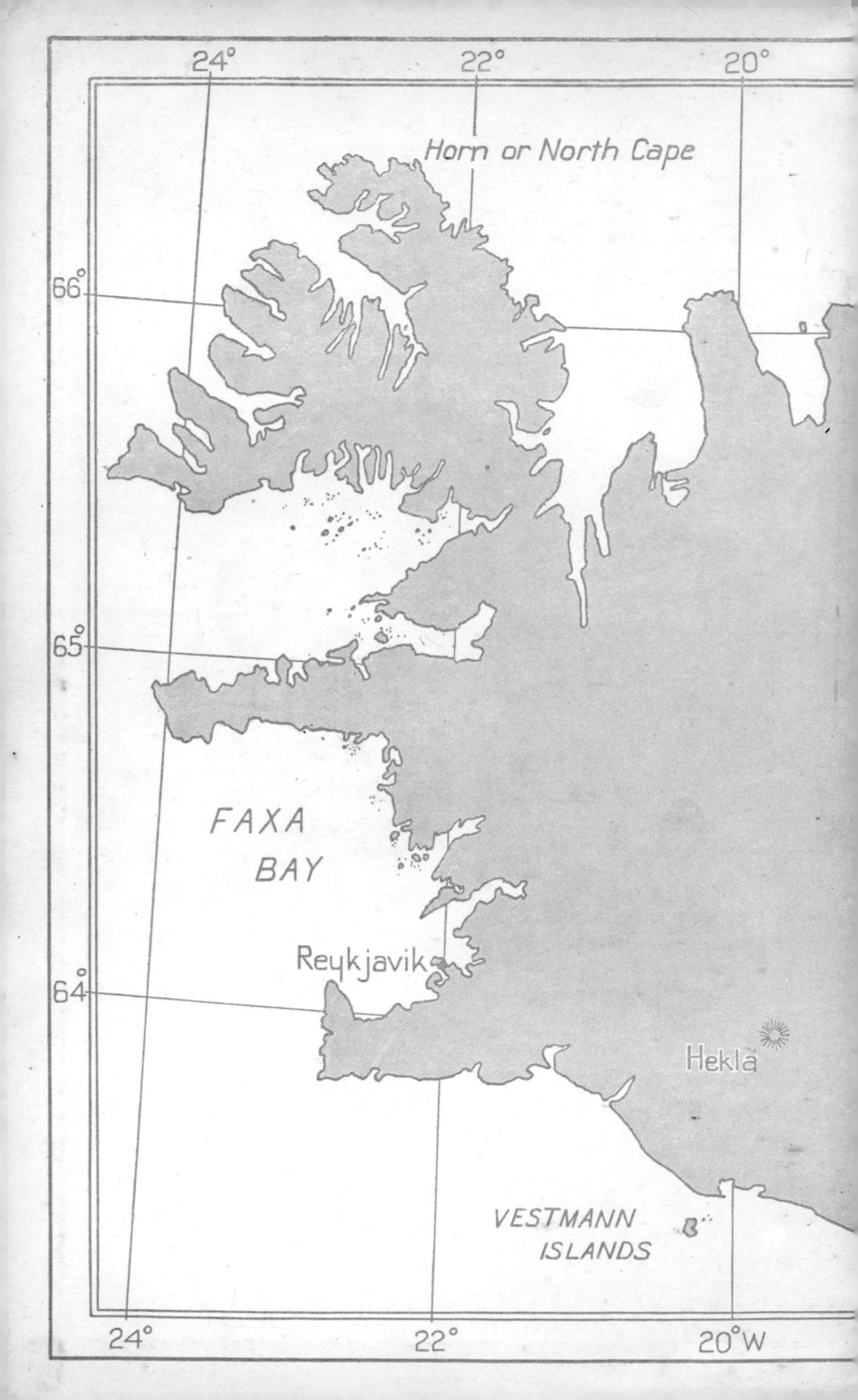
24°
22°
20°
Horn or North Cape
66°
65°
FAXA
BAY
Reykjavik
64°
Hekla
VESTMANN
ISLANDS
24°
22°
20°W